SOME. GROSS

a novel

BIG BRUISER DOPE BOY

...

Something Gross

Copyright © 2021 by Big Bruiser Dope Boy

This is a work of fiction. Names, characters, businesses, places, events, locales, and incidents are either the products of the author's imagination or used in a fictitious manner. Any resemblance to actual persons, living or dead, or actual events is purely coincidental.

No part of this book may be reproduced in any form by any electronic or mechanical means including photocopying, recording, or information storage and retrieval without permission in writing from the author.

ISBN-13: 978-1-7335694-9-1
ISBN-10: 1-7335694-9-9

Cover artwork by G.P. DeSalvo
Author photograph courtesy of Sam Pink

www.apocalypse-party.com

First Edition

Printed in the U.S.A

To anybody in the fight of being who they are

CONTENTS

The First Time Ryan Told Me He Loved Me

Was on New Year's Eve 2018

We had reconnected in mid-December after not talking for three months

He had cut things off between us not long after I told him I loved him

I texted him a long, vitriolic screed, and it "rattled him"

We pretended to ignore each other in bars, and it was getting to feel ridiculous

I sent him a heartfelt apology, and we got dinner at Racine's

Outside, he told me he wanted to keep hanging out, but he was meeting up with his friends, and they still needed to "get the memo"

That was okay, I understood

"I don't really feel like going out anyway"

Later that night, we both ended up at Trade

"You said you weren't going out"

"Yeah, well, after dinner I wanted to decompress"

"You're drunk"

"Yeah"

"Let's go fuck with Evan"

We went to get a drink from Evan and exaggeratedly rubbed tongues outside our mouths in front of him, to his surprise and delight

Things were all good between us, for now

He got drunk and I got drunker and we both got coked-up

We went back to his apartment and had intensely emotional and cathartic make-up sex

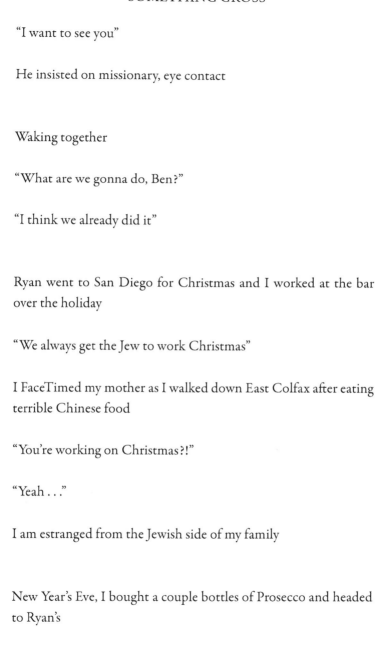

"I want to see you"

He insisted on missionary, eye contact

Waking together

"What are we gonna do, Ben?"

"I think we already did it"

Ryan went to San Diego for Christmas and I worked at the bar over the holiday

"We always get the Jew to work Christmas"

I FaceTimed my mother as I walked down East Colfax after eating terrible Chinese food

"You're working on Christmas?!"

"Yeah . . ."

I am estranged from the Jewish side of my family

New Year's Eve, I bought a couple bottles of Prosecco and headed to Ryan's

Alcohol and cocaine

We went to Zangief and Bernard's, then Trade, then back to Zangief and Bernard's

We kissed at midnight

Things wound down and I extracted Ryan from a conversation he was having with a straight couple

We went back to his place

I was inside him from behind

"Oh Ben, I love you"

He froze

"Stop, stop"

I pulled out

He buried his head under a pillow

I rubbed his back

"Hey, hey, did you just . . ."

I was smiling and chuckling

I lifted the pillow and gently turned his face toward mine

"Hey . . ."

He was groaning and shaking his head

"Hey, it's okay"

He looked at me, tears in his eyes, frowning

"Did you just tell me you love me?"

He nodded woefully

I got emotional

"Those are fighting words—don't say that shit unless you mean it"

"No, I mean it, I love you, Ben"

"I love you, too"

He looked scared

"How long have you felt this way?"

"Since we got back together"

"Have you ever told anyone this before?"

"No"

"Really?"

"Yeah, I've wanted to but never have"

"Wow"

He was forty-four and had never had a boyfriend before, even though he was out since he was eighteen

"I'm honored"

We resumed

We made love

Waking together

"You told me you loved me last night"

He moaned and pushed his head into my chest

SOMETHING GROSS

I texted my friend Joey and told him what happened

"Oh boy, buckle up"

What are we going to do?

What are you going to do, Ryan, when you have already done it?

These are not fighting words

The Road Trip With Joey

Was late spring 2018

Peaches had broken up with me in April, a month before my thesis was due

Until then, I had thought we were moving to New Orleans together after I finished school

We had been together for almost five years

I met Ryan a few weeks after, while Peaches was out of town

I downloaded Scruff for the first time in years

Saw Peaches's profile was logged on at the airport, before he got on the plane to leave

It said he was on PrEP

I took it as permission (not that I needed any) to have sex with whomever I wanted

I traveled from Boulder to Denver to fuck

Ryan was the third, the only "date" I went on

It was more of a hookup under the pretense of a date

Getting drinks first so he could make sure I was not crazy, or catfishing him

Though Ryan was significantly fatter than he was in his pictures

I did not mind that at all

In fact, I preferred it

Because that is something I like

Not the only thing, but one thing

I liked him a lot already

I was still living in Peaches' and my basement apartment, in Boulder

I had helped Peaches move most of his stuff into a storage unit outside town

He was ten years older than I—had more things—so it was pretty bare now

Joey flew in from Austin and I picked him up from the airport in my upstairs roommate's car

I had not seen him in about two years

My best friend

The smartest, funniest person I knew

It was not even close

He came out to see me because he knew I needed it

He needed it, too, but I needed it more

We were to rent a car and drive to Southwest Wisconsin, where my mother's side is from

With a weekend jaunt to Chicago to meet some writer friends— Norm and Seamus—with whom I had spoken online for years but never met in person

Then return to Colorado for a few days

Then drive to Santa Fe to meet Joey's friend for her art installation

Then return to Colorado

Then Joey would leave

It was going to be great

No, it was going to be traumatic and epic, with the potential of us hating each other at the end

If this is not at stake, then what you are on is not a true road trip, and what you have is not true friendship

The energy in the car on the way back from the airport was giddy, manic even

We were psychotic about seeing each other after so long

Laughing, doing voices, making wild and demented faces, brutally and excessively making fun of people in ways they mostly did not deserve

When we laughed, we did not laugh

We held our mouths open widely in silence or faintly perceptible hissing

Faces pained with seizures of muted mirth

It was too much

At one point, I want to say we were both screaming for no reason

There was a reason, though

We loved each other

Joey and I got back to my place and immediately got high with my upstairs roommate

Joints, dabs

We played Mario Kart 64 and I crushed them with my prowess

I smoked them

I crushed, rolled, and then smoked them

Koopa Troopa Beach, Yoshi Valley, Rainbow Road—it did not matter

Joey and I would be on our own rainbow road soon

Except neither of us fucked with rainbows

We tended to wear black

I probably wore black more because of him

He had a black ball cap that said "bootyslayer 69" in cursive on the back

We picked up the car from the rental agency and left

We drove there in one shot

Vaping cannabis distillate

Listening to satellite radio, mostly new wave and disco

Listening to Bruce Springsteen read his autobiography

Which made us cry, the childhood parts

There was also a part where he gave his father pubic lice from sharing the same hotel bathroom

We had to listen to it again, to make sure we heard it right the first time

We did

Bruce Springsteen gave his father crabs

We talked in the car about how I wanted to talk to my family about my growing concern for my mother's cognitive health

Every time I brought it up to her over the last few years, she had attributed it to her aging

Or it was a B-vitamin deficiency, for which her doctor had prescribed her pills

Her coworkers had expressed concern to me

Her friends, too

She should get checked out

It forced her into retirement

When Peaches and I helped her move from Texas to where she grew up, she almost killed two women while driving the rental truck

They chased her down at a rest stop and screamed at her

She refused to let either of us drive the truck because we were not on the insurance

My mother was a dominant, fiercely independent personality

I grew up being scared of her

Her rage was as superhuman as her affection

When my mother drove out to celebrate my finishing school, four years after she retired, she got lost forty-five minutes outside town

She could only describe her immediate surroundings, and not very well

"I'm by a . . . uh . . . um . . . a biiiig uh-place—there's a uhhh—siiiign"

My upstairs roommate's boyfriend, who grew up in the area, deduced that she was parked at a school he knew of

He was right, we found her

She was standing outside her car, looking exhausted and confused

Beautiful gray hair hovering and swirling in high plains gusts

"I'm gonna drive, mom"

"I can drive"

"Yeah I know, but you've been driving all day so I'll drive"

Peaches and I took her to a show at a dinner theater

A show about Patsy Cline, one of her favorites

Sitting across from a mother, father, and a clearly gay tweenage boy

All wearing Disney attire

This family said they had been to the parks, both land and world, over a dozen times

I'm crazy, crazy for feeling so lonely

Driving back, my mother straddled two lanes in the dark, and I pointed it out to her

It was night, she said, and old people had a hard time driving at night

Fair enough

Peaches and I were broken up and trying to show her a good time

She was loudly singing fragments of songs

A few days before Peaches broke up with me, I was FaceTiming with my mother

Telling her our plans to move to New Orleans together

She was so happy, she was crying

Telling her that he broke up with me was intensely painful

I wanted her to feel like I was going to be okay in life

And now I could not give her that, because I was not sure if I would be okay in life

My mother gave me my late grandfather's watch as a graduation gift

We both cried when she gave it to me

I never ended up completing my degree, letting my I/Fs expire over the summer

I did not take my academic advisor's condescending advice and "use the energy" of my breakup

I did not graduate, but I finished school

I was finished with it

I knew I was the best writer in the program at the time (which was not saying much) and probably one of the best writers to ever go through that academy of mainly boarding school brats

Naropa University

Founded by an alcoholic, drug-addicted, womanizing cult leader and his lost, beatnik/hippie devotees

Chögyam Trungpa

And a pedophilic poet

Allen Ginsberg (look up the essay he wrote about becoming a NAMBLA member, or just look at a picture of his face)

A flea clinging to the silver nuthairs of Walt Whitman

Bob Dylan's coattail jockey

He wrote one, maybe two good poems in his entire life

"Howl" is not even that good

"Kaddish"? I would rather get deepthroated by a daikon radish

Howl-about you go fuck yourself?

SOMETHING GROSS

He Kad-dish it out, but he cannot take it

Oh, and while I am at it, suck my dick, Elf Boots

You know who you are

You pompous, vest-wearing douche

Your reading voice is repellant

You have published one book

I have published two, and I am your teenage son's age younger than you

I am writing my third right now

They are all better than yours

I got your "outrider lineage" right here, pal (cups genitals)

I hope your school attains nirvana (goes bankrupt)

I am never making another loan payment

Broke for life, son

My human karma explodes hell into heaven, drags clawing and yelping the devils of delusion back into the reality of God's heart where they were all along

Some people call me Big Bruiser Dope Boy, others call me Ben

You can call me dad

It is nice to meet you

You are late

I am playing

Nobody is good at writing

Joey and I arrived at what was known among my family as "the office," a multipurpose space my grandmother owned that used to be a daycare center

Visiting family would often stay there, and it was used as a gathering space

It still had a bubbler (water fountain)

It was early in the morning

We had a drink, got stoned, and went to bed

We went to my grandmother's house and she was watching a Jacques Brel DVD

Joey was impressed

My mother and aunt were there, too

Joey introduced himself to and delighted my family with his casual brilliance and hilarity

Somewhere in the conversation, my grandmother made a comment about someone she knew, a white guy, having moved to one of the Dakotas to "pretend to be a Native American"

It was hilariously shady/salty

Joey was amazed by her

We got breakfast at the general store

My mother was driving us around with my grandmother in the passenger seat and Joey and me in back

She was acting weird

Making noises and giggling, driving goofily, swerving and braking erratically, defying her almost ninety-year-old mother

Like a misbehaving teenager

It was disturbing and funny

Joey and I looked at each other

Joey and I drove to Dr. Evermore's Sculpture Park outside Baraboo, where my grandmother was originally from

She came from a circus family

There was someone, a great aunt or someone, who used to hang by her long hair from the big top's apex and twirl around

The park was tricky to find, tucked behind a salvage yard, but we found it

It was incredible

The Forevertron was the centerpiece of the park, the largest scrap metal sculpture in the world

Dr. Evermore was the fictive artist persona of Tom Every

A Victorian inventor

SOMETHING GROSS

Per the legend Every created, Dr. Evermore built The Forevertron to blast himself into the cosmos "on a magnetic lightning force beam"

To ride a rainbow road for eternity?

It was too much

There were giant mechanical insects

There was also an area of the park with an orchestra of birds

French horn bodies, trumpet beaks

It was swarming with aggressive mosquitos

Sweltering and muggy

We did not stay for long

Though before we left, we interacted with a woman who lived in a bus, which was also an office, on the park grounds

She represented Every/Evermore

She said he was in a home

Driving into Baraboo, I got lost because neither of our phones had service

I aggressively pulled over, turned around and parked

Joey called it an "angry boyfriend whiparound"

Which diffused the stress instantly because of how funny and perfect of a description it was

We got lunch at a cafe in Baraboo's main square

For dessert, delicious and refreshing espresso milkshakes

They might have had booze in them

On our way back to the Valley, "Back on the Chain Gang" by The Pretenders came on the radio

I found a picture of you, oh oh oh oh
Those were the happiest days of my life

I started to cry because it reminded me of Peaches

I remembered how it came on the radio when we drove his stuff to Boulder so we could move in together

The last two hours of the drive, we went through a wicked storm

We were in his Jeep Wrangler, with a "turtle shell" on top for extra storage

It was extremely windy and we could barely see out the windshield

It was terrifying

We could have died

Joey and I ate at Culver's for the second time

He said he was not used to eating this type of food and it was making him feel like shit/giving him the shits

He ate very "clean" usually

Sometimes he would note how he hated the fact he had to eat to survive

Our food was great

Joey and I drove to Dinah's

A woman in her sixties who was my friend

A drinking buddy and mother figure to me

One of my favorite people ever, who had helped me out during the hardest times of my life

She was graceful, courageous, and kind

Helped other people often, sometimes at her own expense

A bit of a passive-aggressive martyr honestly

But hey, everybody has issues

I met her through her son selling me weed when I was eighteen, working in the Valley after high school

She worked from home

Also at home were Olivia and Orson—Dinah's daughter and her boyfriend

Their daughter Olive, too

Olivia was pregnant with another

Orson was dying of a brain tumor

He was an asshole, I had heard from Dinah and her son

He was from Wimbledon but talked like he was from Brixton

A British [white-person-who-tries-to-"act-black"], essentially

An asshole with a brain tumor (they exist)

He was an InfoWars type guy ("InfoWarrior"?)

He needed your approval while being perpetually antagonistic

I heard he once called Dinah a "cigarette smoking barfly" to her face

You do not say that

You do not say that to your girlfriend's mother while you are staying at her house

Even if it is true

You disrespect Dinah, I stomp your guts wet and flat with the weight of my love for her

Joey and Olive hit it off

Olive, the adorable, precocious toddler

At one point, Joey was reading an illustrated book to her about magical stuff

I was in the other room failing to have a conversation with Orson, who was saying something about something evil in the world, and he got up and went in to check on them

I heard Orson go "Wuh ah yaow shaowing moy choyowd?"

It sounded accusatory

Joey was like ". . . What?"

"Woh doz dat lok loik tah yao?"

"Uhhhhh . . . you mean the wizard?"

"Das a coke gowin een anuvah main's arsehoe"

The illustration, Joey told me later, was of a wizard striding while clutching a scepter

Orson was pointing at the area where the wizard's leg disappeared into his robe

An insidiously subliminal gay pornographic message in the illustrations of a children's book

The book's style of drawing was like paper cutouts, shapes put together

(Why was the asshole a *man's* asshole? (probably because Joey was gay))

He said that shit right in front of his kid!

Orson seemed obsessed with pedophilia

He forbade Olive to be naked around anybody but he and Olivia

Olive would often remove her clothes of her own accord, and he would swiftly police it

He would get mad at Olivia if she had Olive naked in front of anybody

Diapers had to be changed in total seclusion

He talked about it a lot—the global pedophile elite

All this, to Joey and me, meant he was probably secretly a pedophile himself

Now, we were no psychoanalysts, but was this not the mental phenomenon known as "projection"?

The scally doth protest too much, wethinks

Like, okay, yes, the world's wealthiest people operate a sinister network of child trafficking and rape, doing it for perhaps no reasons other than their status affords it and they are powerful enough to do it without getting in trouble, sure, nobody can deny that, but what was with him harping on it?

Made your point, bruv—starting to think this has more to do with your own desires

Was he jealous of them? ("Nowbuh-eee cain woah ah fack moy tew yeewhoa daw-ah bah may!")

He was at least upset that a faggot was getting along with his daughter better than he ever did, and was conflating Joey being gay with . . . Joey wanting to expose his daughter to an image of men having sex with each other?

. . . What?

It was really fucked up, creepy, and sad (one might even say it was too much)

Orson had a scar on his head from a prior surgery

Was not taking doctor's orders, refused treatments, instead opting for self-guided treatments based on things he read online

His forehead would suddenly bead up with sweat periodically

He was such a crazy asshole, and he was dying of a brain tumor (which probably made him even more of a crazy asshole by pressing on the lobe that affected his already shitty personality)

SOMETHING GROSS

About to leave his girlfriend and her mother to raise two children, one of them yet to be born

Children who would live such better lives with their father gone, one barely knowing him and the other not at all, only as a distorted specter of communicated memory

The nicest thing Orson ever did for me was offer me tea

Which, with him being British, was likely more automatic than anything

Dinah drove us and her friend Patty to Madison for dinner and drinks

We went to Mickey's for dinner

Big plates of beef stroganoff on special

Then we went to Caribou Lounge, a dive on East Johnson

We got really, really drunk and stoned

Two women in their sixties, and two gay guys in their twenties and thirties

All making each other laugh

An impenetrable formation

When it was time to go, Joey and I went outside with cigarettes we bummed from Dinah, who had to go to the bathroom, with Patty following behind us

I was pissing in the bushes and heard Joey gasp

"Oh noooo!"

I shook and returned it, pissing in my underwear a little, and went over to see what he was upset about

He was gesturing toward the car

"Look what happened to the car!"

The front bumper had a hole in it, and there were various scuffs and dents

"Oh yeah, that's been there forever"

"What?!"

"Yeah dude, it's not a big deal—drives fine"

"Oh my God!"

He got in the backseat and I joined him

He was livid, arms folded tightly, gaze cast downward, fuming

I was confused, and a little entertained, giggling incredulously, which seemed to enrage him all the more

"Dude, it's really fine—I don't know what you're so upset about—relax"

"DON'T TELL ME TO RELAX! THERE'S A FUCKING HOLE IN THE CAR!"

Patty got in the passenger seat

"Joey, that's been there for years"

"WHAT?! HOW IS THAT EVEN POSSIBLE?!"

"I don't know man, she hit something or it came like that"

He clenched his jaw and shook his head, seethingly exhaling

He seemed inordinately irate and despairing not only about the longstanding damage that had been there as far back as I could remember, such that it was characteristic of the car—it made Dinah's car Dinah's car—but also because Patty and I were not having meltdowns about it

"This is so bad—I don't know what we're gonna do—this is so fucked . . . WHAT THE HELL IS ALL THIS SHIT?! IT'S FILTHY BACK HERE!!!"

He was looking around at Dinah's gardening equipment, small square plastic pots and topsoil scattered and stained into the floor carpeting

"Yeah, that's Dinah's stuff, she's a bit messy, so what?"

"WHY THE FUCK IS IT IN THE CAR?!?!?!"

"DUDE, because . . . wait . . . do . . . oh my God"

I realized Joey was so drunk and stoned that he thought Dinah's car was the rental

A completely different make, model, color, and year of production than Dinah's

"Joey, this isn't the rental, this is Dinah's car . . ."

"Oh my God"

He put his face in his hands and started laughing

"Oh my God . . . oh my God"

I was screaming

We were back at the office with Dinah

Super drunk, passing around a bottle of whiskey

Joey put on a YouTube video of Crowded House playing "Don't Dream It's Over"

The last concert of their farewell tour, and the last song of that concert

The last time, at the time, they would all play that song together

There's a battle ahead, many battles are lost
But you'll never see the end of the road while you're traveling with me

Dinah wanted to leave, but Joey and I stopped her because she was too drunk

She passed out on the couch and was gone when we woke

Joey and I drove the rental to Chicago and parked it in a garage in Lincoln Park

We had booked a hotel room for two nights

Our hotel seemed to have just undergone a renovation, making it look new and cheap, with pseudo-artsy shit all over that was supposed to be representative of the city

We learned Seamus was staying in a hotel down the block and across the street

Everybody was going to meet in Seamus's hotel room

Norm, Lance (a publisher who had put out books from both Norm and Seamus), Truck (a writer), and others

I did not know anybody other than Norm and Seamus

The hotel was old, smelly, and charming

We got to Seamus's room and he offered us absinthe

His attire seemed to emulate Anton LaVey

Norm and the others arrived

Norm looked at me, said "dude," and embraced me with his broad, robust frame

He had always felt like a kind of older brother to me

An encouraging, quiet example

Not only did I love and admire his writing, but he showed me possibilities of how I could live in the world and make art

We also seemed to have a bit of a "twinsies" dynamic, us both being Geminis (just kidding)

Our values overlapped, as did our humor

I think, among other things, we initially bonded over failing to function normally in society

We even looked related (in the years since, as we have spent more time together in person, people have mistaken us for biological brothers with such frequency—sometimes insisting on it in disappointed disbelief when told we are not—that it is now fully expected and enjoyed)

It was wonderful to finally see my friends

Seamus dispensed gifts to the group

Books he curated towards what he knew of their individual recipients' interests, as well as copies of his latest for each

An incredibly thoughtful and touching gesture

"Damn, thanks a lot man"

"This is so sweet of you"

"You shouldn't have"

"It's too much"

Nobody else had brought gifts

I had brought weed, but that was just as much for me as it was for everybody else

Norm asked Seamus if he could print something in the lobby

Norm was giving a reading at a bookstore from his newest offering that evening

We had dinner at a restaurant close by and walked to the bookstore

It was in a bougie neighborhood and had a large gay section

It seemed like a gay bookstore, rainbow flags mounted on its facade

Norm broke off and talked to the event's organizers, who appeared frantically deferential about getting him bottled water

I had to go to the bathroom, but could not find it, so I asked the handsome clerk where it was

He flirtatiously apprised me of its cranny

I went to the bathroom and before entering had to quickly dodge being bludgeoned by its narrowly-accessed, tightly-springed door as somebody exited

I found Joey and Seamus in the gay section, which I started to halfheartedly browse

Joey told me the clerk who flirted with me was a dick to him, acting irritated he was being addressed at his job

He treated customers differently based on whether or not he was attracted to them

Classic shallow gay guy behavior

I looked around at the books in the gay section, feeling disdain for contemporary gay people

Whatever it was I glanced in the matte and gloss of the covers, I felt neither a part of, nor did I want to join

I felt alienated by it

A stranger within my own named desires

Your sad, deep gay story does not make you any more interesting, special, or worthy of love

BIG BRUISER DOPE BOY

You still have to work

You still have to be a person

Norm came over and looked at us with wide eyes

"That bathroom door . . . I wasn't ready for it"

"Yeah, it's a doozy"

He pointed to the books and grinned

"You gonna be there someday bro?"

He knew how I felt about it

Norm's reading was great

We went to a bar after, played some pool

Lance seemed upset about something

Truck seemed jolly, if brooding

Seamus, a gloomy, Burroughs-esque, wraithlike presence

Norm was averse to the atmosphere of bars

It was clear he was only in one to be a gracious host

Having worked in bars, I identified with him, but maybe, being gay, had put up with more for the sake of being around "people like me"

He mentioned how he was avoiding looking at the screens of TVs and game machines

Joey and I thought about picking up Big Buck Hunter's plastic pump-action shotgun and digitally dispatching zebras like the others, but it did not feel like the right time or place

We were there to see Norm and Seamus

The group dispersed and Joey and I went back to our hotel room

Before falling asleep, I found Dean on Scruff

Dr. Dean Campbell

A muscle daddy bear from San Francisco in an open marriage

I had hooked up with him in 2013 in Madison, two weeks before moving home with my mother in Austin and two months before I met Peaches

He had crossed my mind from time to time

I messaged him

"Dean!"

"Well well, I suppose it was bound to happen eventually"

We agreed for me to go over to his hotel room early in the morning

I set an alarm for 6:00 AM

"Hey"

Joey stirred

I was fully dressed, trying to whisper

"What's up?"

He was hungover

"Hey, sorry to wake you up, but I'm gonna go—I'll be back in a couple hours tops"

"Where are you going?"

"I'm gonna meet up with this guy at his hotel downtown . . . to have sex—I know him from years ago, he just happens to be in town"

"Oh . . . okay . . . have fun I guess"

We were chuckling a little, he awkwardly and I sheepishly

"Thanks, sorry to wake you up, I just don't want you to worry if you wake up and I'm not here"

"It's fine"

"I need this—oh, wanna get breakfast at that pancake place when I get back?"

"Sure, whatever, I'm going back to sleep now"

"He's a pretty cool guy actually"

"I'm glad, goodnight"

"He works for a big pharmaceutical company . . . okay . . . bye . . . . . . love you"

I slunk out the door

Dean was as sexy as ever, and fun enough, but it was different—I had not been able to shake my brain of Ryan, an erotically ideal, seemingly perfect sexual partner with whom I felt a strong emotional and mental connection

Our session was brought to an abrupt halt after I knowingly prematurely ejaculated inside him without a condom (he was on PrEP), promising to get hard again "in like two minutes"—he was sitting on me and, as he stood, I felt something warmer than usual

Joey and Seamus were waiting for me in a booth at The Original Pancake House

I slid onto the bench next to Joey

". . . Everything okay?"

"Yeah—have y'all ordered?"

"Not yet"

I turned the menu's pages while furtively smelling my fingers

"What are y'all getting?"

Joey was getting an omelette, and Seamus, as he did at dinner last night, was not getting anything

During his travels, he adhered to a stringent diet of what he referred to as his "nubbins" (dry snacks with low digestive impact)

He had mentioned his health issues to me before

Seamus was a bonafide artist and eccentric—I could feel the electricity of his obsessiveness because I had that in me, too

He was a genuine person—hypersensitive and soulful with a terminally dour edge

His commitment to doing exactly what he did had always impressed me, how he constructed sonically, syntactically, and semantically dense and gnarled lines and sentences that masterfully hit your guts as grounded in experience without ever producing the obscure, impenetrable, risk-free, interchangeable textual wallpaper of many of his pussyfooted, jealous peers—he knew who he was and was not afraid of showing it—there was something of himself at stake in all his work

I decided on a skillet and excused myself to the bathroom

I washed my hands twice in hot water, after which they still smelled like what they smelled like

We ate and left The Original Pancake House, returning to our respective hotel rooms, after which we were to reconvene and walk to Millennium Park to meet up with Norm and his younger brother Nicola as well as Lance and the others

Joey was rinsing his mouth out after brushing his teeth

"I'm gonna shower—that guy shit on my dick and I can't get the smell off"

He spat in the sink

"Ew, fucking *gross* . . . I knew something was going on with you—fucking fidgeting all breakfast"

He wiped his mouth and I followed him to his suitcase

"It's like there are particles of it inside my nose or something"

"Oh my God stop"

I was giggling

"Either that or the shit, like, fused to my skin"

He winced and pushed his fingers into his brow, slowly shaking his head as he spoke through his teeth

"I hate you so much"

"I already washed my dick like four times in a row there, but I feel like I can still smell it"

"That's so *fucking* disgusting—it's like it's in your mind . . . you're like Lady Macshit"

"Here"

I reached toward his face and he recoiled, leaping onto his bed, crouching and clenching his fists in what can only be described as an "Italian-American martial arts stance"

"FUCK you get the FUCK away from me take a GODDAMN shower!"

Joey, Seamus, and I walked a long way through miserable heat to Millennium Park, navigating the zoo and its surrounding park, tourists, children, bicycles, a guy saying we looked like we were going to a metal concert, a Black Hebrew Israelite calling us "white devils," etc., stopping twice at convenience stores for water and air-conditioning

We settled in the shade and waited for Norm and Nicola

A guy walked up and provided us with unsolicited tourism information for a minute, then asked for money

Seamus offered him some "nubbins" and he declined

Norm and Nicola arrived

They had a soccer ball with them and suggested we kick it around

We went to an open area of grass and spread out

Seamus participated for a few go-rounds, then sat on a bench, looking severely displeased

After, we took turns putting our heads under a water fountain

We left Millennium park, started walking toward a neighborhood to get Italian ices

Nicola did various martial arts moves on sidewalk objects

Crossing a bridge over the river, Norm double thumbs-downed and stared at a barge of tourists as it blew its horn and passed beneath

After, I saw him appear to psychically/emotionally connect with a leashed dog in passing, subtly putting his hand out to be sniffed, without acknowledging its owner at all

The ices were still far, so Nicola ordered a car

They were delicious and refreshing

We went into a deli and got some sandwiches and beverages

It was nice to sit down and eat in a climate-controlled deli

We talked, among other things, about the TV show *Family Matters*, starring the great Reginald VelJohnson

We improvised imagining Steven Urkel in bleak contemporary cinema scenarios, for instance, if he was tasked by the state to do some form of espionage in the Middle East (mushroom cloud in distance, him saying "did I do that?" and so on)

We were cracking each other up

I smelled my fingers

Paging Dr. Campbell

It was faint, but still there

The unwashable residue of my tragic aspiration for bottom bears

Out, damned daddy doo-doo!

It was getting later in the afternoon and into the early evening, so we arranged to meet up with Lance and the others, who had been doing some tourist activities that day, at a bar by Seamus's hotel

Norm said he had money on his public transit card and we could take the train back

Walking to the platform, we were passed by a convertible blasting "(Don't Fear) The Reaper" by Blue Öyster Cult with four young people in it

Norm noted the irony

The fear of death was surely present in the convertible, the song itself and its excessive volume demonstrating the transparent denial and concealment of that fear

The train car was humid and packed with people

Nicola poised himself to get off and so did Joey

Norm stopped him

"We're getting off at the next stop"

"Oh, why is Nicola getting off?"

"He's going to stop by his work"

"I'll meet up with you guys later"

Nicola disclosed to me that he was going to stop by the gym where he worked because he felt an oncoming bowel movement, the urgency of which was too profound for him to believe he could last another stop without soiling himself on the crowded train car

He was wearing athletic shorts

I started laughing with him, imagining his coworkers and gym members trying to talk to him, unknowingly and maybe catastrophically impeding his desperate mission

It was funny, but I could tell he was in moderate physical discomfort, focusing on not shitting himself

If I could have helped him hold it in, I would have

That came out wrong

So did that

We were walking through Wrigleyville at dusk, right next to the stadium

Norm turned to me

"I hate it here, but it's not that bad when there are so few people around"

We passed a guy in a suit who had an earpiece in

"Still enough people for the CIA, I guess"

He laughed

"I noticed that guy too"

I put my finger to my ear and made a radio feedback noise

"We got four suspicious goons, over"

He laughed

"Four suspicious goons . . ."

The bar was in a basement down a flight of stairs and we were relieved to find it

We played pool at first, then darts

We were getting very drunk

Seamus was over playing games of any kind

I overheard Lance condescendingly pitching him a novel to write called "Pig Man" about some asshole finding redemption

It was painful—he was basically calling him a bigot to his face in the form of a book pitch

At one point, Lance asked Joey and me if we were writers

We told him we were, and that was that

Nothing here for you, boss

It was embarrassing to see him stewing about Norm not giving him enough attention

I felt bad for Norm

But I supposed that was the social price you paid when you made art that nobody else could make: other people wanted things from you that you could not give them, projecting onto you their desires, insecurities, and warped ideas of you, themselves, and the world

What I admired most about Norm was how he kept to himself and did not entertain other people's bullshit, even if they expected something from him because they published his books

Publishers were so often like that—using their often inherited wealth to position themselves in proximity to art and the authentic individuals who produced it, idealizing and valorizing yet resenting and coveting them for being who they were and wanting what they had

They wanted to be friends without having anything meaningful in common

I was having a great time playing darts

Lance, Seamus, and the others left

Norm and Nicola offered to walk us to the hotel

We shared a joint on the corner

Hugs and goodbyes were exchanged

In the hotel room, from our beds, Joey and I went through everything that had happened

In the morning, Joey realized he did not have his debit card in his wallet

"Goddamnit, I knew I wouldn't get out of here without a fucking scratch"

He called the bar we were at last night

They had it

We got his card back, checked out of the hotel, and drove back to Wisconsin

SOMETHING GROSS

At the office, I was worried I had gonorrhea

I kept going to the bathroom to check if I had a discharge

I would squeeze the sides of my penis head so my external urethral orifice would open, and then I would drag my finger along the underside of my shaft like getting the last toothpaste out of its tube

I thought I saw something

Maybe

I needed a second opinion

I asked Joey to come into the bathroom with me to look

Joey had never seen my penis before

"I mean, I can't really tell—if it's bothering you that much just get tested"

"I'm sorry I asked you to look at my dick"

"I guess a boundary has been crossed, but it's whatever"

It was Sunday

I made Joey drive me to the emergency room in Madison

In the emergency room, the nurse treated me for gonorrhea and chlamydia prophylactically

I would find out the results of my urine panel in a day or two

I also got a rapid HIV test

It had been years, because I had been monogamous with Peaches (except when we were long-distance and he cheated on me before a visit and gave me gonorrhea and Pink eye in both eyes at the same time, but we worked through that)

I was waiting for the results, silently coddling my ears as I often did when I was anxious

I was sitting on the examination bench and Joey was sitting in a chair

I heard his phone make the Grindr notification message

He grimly looked up from his phone at me without moving his head

How dare you, Joey

How dare you taint the sanctity of the emergency room and my hypochondria

The nurse came back and the result was negative

We met Dinah, Olivia, Orson, and Olive at an Indian buffet in Madison

On the way in, I said something that made Joey laugh

A guy hanging with his friends outside noticed us

"Nice smile"

"Thanks"

Once inside, Joey turned to me

"That guy totally just flirted with me"

"Yeah, that was really cute"

I had to get food in me fast to help the antibiotics be easier on my stomach

I piled my plate up and sat in the booth

I had a few bites, then excused myself, looking at Joey gravely

"Yep, here it comes"

It started coming out as I bent my knees, before my haunches made contact with the toilet seat

It was the most incredible diarrhea I had ever experienced

Suggesting a kind of endlessness

Volume-wise, it was otherworldly

It just kept going

Like Rainbow Road

It was surely as colorful

Where was it all coming from?

It was awe-inspiring

And yes, it was too much

In the ferocity of the moment, I ceased to be human and became a hollow cylinder expelling the sordid waste of a molecular war

I slid the enlightened husk of my flesh back in the booth

". . . Everything okay?"

"Indeed"

Orson's forehead was sweating and he was talking about regular, everyday stuff

I am playing—he was talking about the malevolent forces at work in the world

He said something about China, then started talking about Russia

"Yew now een Rosha, twanzgenda paypoh ah geh-in twanspwantz fwum bahfalow vajoynaz" ("You know in Russia, transgender people are getting transplants from buffalo vaginas")

I was not sure what to say

I mean, what do you say to that, other than "I hope you find the peace in death you never found in life"?

"Uhh—It's good they're using every part of the buffalo, I guess"

A bit of food fell from Dinah's mouth as she laughed

Joey and Olivia giggled

Orson stared at me blankly

Olive did not care about any of us, because she was a transcendent genius

Joey and I were going back to Boulder in a couple days and I had still not brought up my concerns about my mother to the rest of my family

We were going to dinner at my aunt and uncle's house that night and I told Joey I was going to linger and bring it up to them there

After dinner, after my mother left, I asked my aunt into the other room and told her I was worried about my mother's memory

She told me my mother had early onset dementia

I started to cry

My grandmother came into the room and joined the conversation

My mother had been diagnosed two years ago

My family did not tell me

They had been waiting for me to bring it up to them

I had to live my life, they said, and my mother's quality of life was okay

SOMETHING GROSS

Joey came in and noticed I was crying

"What's going on?"

"She has dementia"

"What?"

"Yeah"

"Fuck . . ."

My family and I resolved to not emotionally bypass each other anymore

My grandmother told me we would not avoid it

We would plan things together as a team

In the rental, on the way back to the office, Joey told me how proud of me he was

"You handled that with grace"

From bed, I texted Ryan

"I found out tonight my mom has dementia—I know you've been through a similar horror—it would be nice to talk about it with you"

After having sex on our first "date," Ryan and I went to Pete's Kitchen, a twenty-four-hour Greek diner on Colfax

He told me that his mother had died of Alzheimer's and Parkinson's nine months previous, and that after, he "ran away" to Colorado, where he had lived and gone to school before

He told me how he had been unemployed for two years, leaving his job when his mother got really bad

I was almost crying telling him about Peaches's and my still very fresh breakup

When he dropped me off at Union Station to take the bus back to Boulder, I thanked him and told him I really liked him, that I needed a friend

I wanted to be his friend

Ryan texted me back

"I'm so sorry to hear that, Ben—you're right, it is a horror—of course, we can talk about it whenever you want"

SOMETHING GROSS

I called Peaches and told him

He cried and had questions for which I had no answers

My grandmother, mother, Joey, and I were at the general store the next morning, eating breakfast

I could not look at my mother the same way

Or myself

Sure, she had been masking her symptoms to others and herself with increasing ineptitude

But I had been in denial, too

I did not take action

I had to, as my family had rationalized to me, live my life

I was a deadbeat son

Like my deadbeat father

My mother could tell I was looking at her differently

She was still acutely intuitive in sensing other people's emotions

Who knows, maybe she was even more perceptive with the other things falling away

She opened a copy of the local small town newspaper

She pointed to something

"Look"

She started reading it aloud, slowly

It was like she was trying to prove to us she did not have dementia

Part of the masking, too, being the loss of the awareness that the world of your mind's language is crumbling around you

People sometimes couch it as a reversion to a childlike innocence, and that's a nice thought

But from the outside looking in, it was suffering and confusion

I was trying not to cry just looking at her

Outside the general store, she confronted me

"What's wrong?"

". . . Nothing—I just love you"

Now I was doing the masking, and she was seeing through it

"It's fine—I'm fine"

"Yeah, I know"

She gave me a hug

"I love you"

"I love you so much"

My urine panel results came back—I never had anything

My grandmother, mother, Joey, and I had dinner at a restaurant in town that night

At some point during our meal, my grandmother was approached by two men, unmistakably an elderly gay couple

"OH MY GOODNESS!"

She stood up and hugged them both, smiling bigger than I had ever seen her smile

They were clearly old friends

It was poignantly joyful

Joey started crying

I felt bad for having dragged him, albeit unknowingly, through such trauma

He was raw from it and reacting tenderly to things

I know I was

Seeing him cry made me start to cry

Too, too much

I tweeted about having found out about my mother's illness

Some asshole retweeted me with the comment: "totally chill to broadcast this on the internet"

Norm texted me

"I'm really sorry to hear about your mom—if you need to talk about it I'm here—my nonna had dementia—love you bro"

Norm was there for me when Peaches broke up with me, too

I texted him and Joey the morning after it happened

They were my best friends

The rest of the world could choke on its sponsored algorithm

They were both my brothers and my boyfriends

Except I loved them more deeply than I could ever love a boyfriend

They appreciated me for who I was, not who they expected me to be to satisfy themselves

They could feel me

They knew I did not have anybody else like them in my life

Joey and I drove back to Colorado, forever changed by everything, our friendship as close as it had ever been

Holding onto each other in the alone-stream of the perfectly merciless universe

We still had to go to Santa Fe, which, with our drained energies, we had our doubts about, but were still committed

Ride or die, for better or worse, for nothing, for what

For anything *but* kicks

Fuck Jack Kerouac, fuck jazz, and fuck America

Fuck spoken word poetry, fuck brunch, and fuck community

Fuck fake-ass, pussy-ass writers and their chummy poser publishers, fuck the dog and its leash, fuck the fishes and the water they swim in and pretend to breathe

Fuck the CIA—I am the CIA

Fuck me, fuck you

Fuck every reality and counter-reality

Fuck the continents and their cultures, the senses and empirical knowledge

Fuck the twisted thought-demons guarding the gates of direct perception

Fuck the relative and the absolute

Fuck it all to sublime, empty nowhere

SOMETHING GROSS

Fuck Goddamnit motherfucking FUCK

We had a couple days, though, to "relax" before driving down there

Joey and I went for a walk at Sawhill Ponds to watch birds

He could identify most birds, and I could identify very few

We saw one he had not seen before, but guessed it was a golden oriole

Walking back to the car, Joey paused and turned around and looked at me

"I'm really happy we're doing this together"

He wiped sweat from under my eye with his thumb

I walked ahead, then paused and turned around and looked at him

"I'm sorry, but that freaked me out a little—it seemed like you were about to kiss me or something—I need you to be my friend"

"Fuck, sorry, I'm just emotional—yeah, that was weird"

"It's okay—I love you"

"I love you, too"

I met Joey not long after I met Peaches, through a mutual friend we both despise

It was at a small house party

Joey was blackout drunk, dominating the song selection, aggressively dancing and lip-synching at people, getting inches from their faces

New Year's Eve that year, 2013, as our friendship was blooming, we were at a party at the same house where we met

He was there with his ex, blackout drunk

Toward the end of the night, he leaned in to kiss me

We argue over if our lips actually made contact—I say we kissed for a second, and he says we did not

I rejected him, grabbing his shoulders

I was already in love with Peaches

I felt bad—he was very embarrassed

Despite him being a hilarious, brilliant, beautiful, sexy person, I could not fathom him as a sexual partner

Or, I could, but that was behind a door I would never open

It was not as if I had not been flirting with him—I absolutely was—but I was not flirting with him as a means to more, and therein laid the misunderstanding

He was a gorgeous human being, but I had a type, and he was not it

He would tell me that having a type was basic or less evolved, that it meant you had not done the work to break down dominant conventions within yourself and open up, same as being either a total top or bottom in the "binary"

But I had never tried to innovate or break the mold with my desires

I wanted what I wanted, was driven by that which I was driven— social critiques be damned

He said he did not have a type, despite, from what I could tell, him inevitably becoming boyfriends with guys as skinny or skinnier than he was

He once told me his ex had "Jafar hands"

Back in the basement, watching Golden Girls, I noticed he got goosebumps on his legs after laughing at something Estelle Getty said to Bea Arthur

I stood up and noted this, still reeling from the weird, intense, emotional moment between us at the ponds

He got really self-conscious, then angry at me, then made fun of me

Did I think that because he got goosebumps watching Golden Girls with me that he was turned on by me or something?

I was paranoid—about what our friendship was, how he maybe felt about me and how I maybe felt about him, but could not admit

He clowned on me until the awkwardness passed

I apologized for freaking out

What we went through in the Midwest had deepened and darkened our bond

Our friendship was charged with passionate tension

It exceeded the threshold of easily digestible experience (it was too much)

Peaches had seemed to resent our friendship sometimes

He was my life partner whom I seldom touched—only for hellos, goodbyes, and when either something really happy or sad had happened

We drove to Santa Fe, the landscape of which recalled the roadrunner and coyote cartoons

It was naturally beautiful and culturally repugnant

Rich people swarming around municipally mandated adobe architecture

Shopping and food, turquoise and booze

We attended his friend's art installation, which was in a big complex

It was cool enough, but it was also a lame, tryhard status event, like virtually anything occurring in a gallery

"Whenever I'm at a thing like this, I always think 'where's the shooter gonna come from?'"

His friend invited us to a fancy spa in the mountains, but we declined

His friend invited us to a conceptual art playground-museum

called Meow Wolf, but we declined

We drove to a petroglyphs site outside town

It was extremely dry and hot—the sun rays palming my head

We walked the trail and up the rock formations and saw the ancient carvings

There were many of them, with a few main locations

He pointed at one and told me it was Kokopelli, a fertility deity

He talked about how petroglyphs differed from hieroglyphs

"They're not language—they're just like . . . something some guy did when he was bored"

"Maybe he was on peyote"

"Yeah, maybe, who knows . . ."

Walking the trail back to the parking lot, I smiled

"Race you back to the car"

"Hell no—it's so hot"

"Yeah, you're right"

I started walking faster

So did Joey

We started sprinting and laughing

He yelled

"Your legs are so fucking long!"

I won

We hunched over and panted by the car

I was dehydrated and heat-exhausted

I was shivering

I had goosebumps

We drove back to Boulder

We returned the rental

The night before Joey's flight out, he was sleeping upstairs and I was awake downstairs

Ryan had come from Denver to hang out with some of his Boulder friends

He came over after

We got naked—cuddled and talked

It was great to see him again

I mentioned my mother, and he looked at me like he did not know what I was talking about

"... She was diagnosed with early onset dementia"

"—Oh, right, sorry!"

How could he not remember such a connective thing between us?

Maybe it was too much for him

It kind of made me feel like an asshole with a brain tumor

I told him my family had not told me for two years

"They should have told you"

"Yeah, I was mad at first, but I let it go because it wouldn't do anybody any good—they told me they were waiting for me to bring it up to them"

"Yeah . . . 'you have to live your life' and all that"

"Oh my God—that's exactly what they said!"

He closed his eyes and nodded

We held and kissed each other

He told me he had a theory that childhood trauma made a person more likely to develop symptoms later in life

I told him my mother had been raped when she was six years old by a family friend who was babysitting her

She told me about it when I was a teenager

She woke with him inside her, and he told her he would "get her" if she told anybody

Ryan told me his mother had been raped when she was a child, too

I told him that, when she was a teenager and the man who raped her was dead, my mother told my grandmother what had happened to her, and my grandmother got up and left the room without saying a word, and that she did the same exact thing in a family therapy session decades later

"Maybe it was too much for her, the guilt—also, that's a different generation—I'm not sure people talked about that stuff like that back then"

"That's her mom, though—that's when you hold your child and go 'oh baby, I'm so sorry, I love you'"

Ryan thought parental love was universal and unconditional—not cultural and temporal

An ironic thing for a person with a Master's degree in anthropology to say

Still, I wanted him to be right

I thanked him for coming over

In the morning, I drove Joey to the airport in my roommate's car

We hugged tightly outside the terminal

I was sad to see my friend leave

But driving back home, alone, it was not too much

SOMETHING GROSS

Life and death were not—are not—too much

And I can only will myself to change so much

When so much change happens on its own

I meet you in the middle of this road without edges

Where there are no words or thoughts

Some people call me Big Bruiser Dope Boy, others call me Ben

Joey calls me Benji

Norm calls me Lurky

My father calls me on holidays

My mother calls me by her brother's name now

But I can tell she still knows who I am

You forget the most important things last

The most important things last

Pride 2018 and the Ensuing Bullshit

I was planning on meeting Ryan at the Denver Wrangler on Pride Sunday for the beer bust

The last day of operation for the failing bar in its ill-conceived location

I took the bus using my school pass, which still worked

I had texted Ryan earlier that week about meeting up

Wanting to seem non-pushy, because it was Pride

You do you—sexual freedom and all that language spoken by grown men to give themselves permission to act as groups of feral, horny children

SOMETHING GROSS

He told me he would be at the bar and we could see each other

I was going there to see him

But he was not going there to see me—not specifically

I got to Union Station earlier in the day and decided to kill time eating a burger

I sat at the restaurant bar, feeling sorry for myself

I was single on Pride for the first time in five years

Trying to see a guy I wanted to see more than he wanted to see me

Drinking a mug of beer, waiting for my burger, I idly spun around on my barstool

I noticed a man sitting alone in the booth behind and across from me

He did not have a nose, just a hole where his nose would have been

It jarred things into perspective

I may have not had a boyfriend, but I did have a nose

I was suddenly grateful

Without a nose, I could not smell

While waiting to see how this man would go about drinking his beverage, my burger was set in front of me

Ryan texted me that he would be getting to the Wrangler around 5:00

It was 2:00, and it was raining

So I rode the light rail around, watching people walking to, from, and through the festivities

I got to the Wrangler around 4:00

It was really busy and crazy, so many people—a blowout

I had hardly spent any time in Denver when I was with Peaches, in Boulder

Except for trimming unregulated weed in a warehouse for cash in an industrial area

Or visiting my friend Layla, a former classmate of mine who worked as a ProDomme while getting trained as a sex therapist

With one visit to the Wrangler for Pride

I did not know anybody there

I waited in a long line in the rain for a drink

Ryan texted me that he would be getting to the bar late

I stood under a tree and did not talk to anybody, sipping my drink slowly, because I was broke

Ryan showed around 5:45

He was wearing a purple t-shirt with the white silhouette of a unicorn on it

He had been partying since Thursday

We hugged

He went to an ATM

I stood around, not talking to anybody

He came back with his friend Ron, a cute blonde cub with a septum piercing

He had an adorable butterball face like Peaches's

He was from Virginia, like Ryan

"D.C. cunts" Ryan called himself and Ron

Ryan left and I tried to make conversation with Ron

I asked him what his "livelihood" was

"Are you asking me what I do for work?"

"Yes"

"I'm an interior designer"

"Oh cool—my ex does that"

"Cool"

SOMETHING GROSS

Ryan came back with his friend Chad, a taller skinny guy with a pot belly and bad teeth

He was chewing gum

He seemed to be on ecstasy, maybe cocaine

Some asshole was splashing around in a big rain puddle close to us

Ryan told him to stop, but he did not listen

It was cold for mid-June

It was my twenty-eighth birthday, as well as Father's Day

Our group moved to the edge of a tent under which a large crowd was dancing

I did not feel like dancing

Another friend of Ryan's showed—Bernard

A lithe younger guy with long blonde hair blooming from a visor

He danced in place, said something forgettably sassy, and went along

Ryan said that, last night, Bernard was really fucked up so he gave him a ride home

He said he was crying to Bernard about his mother

Ryan hunched his shoulders and folded his arms, telling me he was cold

I rubbed his chest and back with my hands

He pushed his head into my chest, then looked at me

"Ben—I hope you don't find this patronizing—I like getting naked with you and cuddling and all that, but you know we're not gonna get married or anything, right?—I'm older than you and you live in Boulder—An old man like me would suck the life out of you, anyway"

"Yeah . . ."

"Okay, cool"

He snorted cocaine from a red metal application device and offered me some

I declined

"Oh—I see someone I know—be right back"

"Okay"

Ryan showed me a profile off a fetish app on his phone, a person he knew

This person had their genitals surgically removed

I acknowledged it, and Ryan said he knew he could show it to me because I was open and not judgmental

I hung out for a little while longer, then took the bus back to Boulder

I could not sleep that night

I sent a long text to Ryan

> *I've been thinking about this thing you said and how it made me feel and why you might have said it. At the bar you started by saying something like "I don't mean to be/I hope this isn't patronizing, but" and then you cited a difference in*

age and location, pointing to an impossibility of "marriage" and ending with how we'd be friends. I think it surprised me—not that you said that stuff, but it surprised me how much it stung to hear that, and to imagine what you might have observed, intuited, or assessed about me that would make you feel the need to communicate that, that made me feel kind of embarrassed for being foolish, or something. I think it surprised me because I hadn't realized I'd taken to you in such a way that hearing it would produce a twinge. I don't at all mean to say that I've wanted marriage, with you or anyone, and I'm so disappointed to hear that I won't someday be getting married, haha. No, I think I'd feel grateful and lucky to be a friend to you. But man, I didn't know until I thought about what you said and how it made me feel that I had developed an intimate regard for you to the degree that your rhetorical (and yeah patronizing, but I don't think that's bad or wrong necessarily: people patronize/ condescend to each other all the time—it's fine and it maybe even serves some greater societal function(?)—maybe I'll get to patronize you someday . . . if I'm not doing it right now) preclusion of the possibility of what I'll call a "relatively longer-term relationship" was a bit of a sheepish bummer. Not even to say that I want to be your boyfriend, or anyone's goddamn boyfriend. It is a great relief, after so long, to not be that for another person. I'm a solitary guy who gets lasting, meaningful pleasure and enjoyment out of working alone on creative projects in a way that I imagine people who are really social and party a lot get from being really social and partying a lot. I don't mean to put that down at all, but this is how I'm relating to it. I have to imagine the people doing that are deep down looking for the same shit, the same feelings I am. Anyway—that you explicitly clarified your terms, in what I heard tonally as a kind of letting me down easy early, because pragmatism, because let's be realistic, because you're there and I'm here, because you're this and I'm that—it did kind of hurt. Not in a way I can't get past, though. But in a way that I do want to tell you about, being friends and all. The age gap thing. I don't know what to say. With both friends and lovers, I've ended up with, gravitated towards, those older than me, which is to say people in their mid-to-late thirties, their forties. I'm not going to psychoanalyze myself to figure out why that is (I have a couple cute theories), because I don't think it matters why. Sure, I have "daddy issues" (name me a person with a father who doesn't have "daddy issues" so I can please shake their hand), but I'm not looking for a "daddy" (again, not to look down on those who are) which is another dimension of what makes my situation hard. I'm not looking for whatever that dynamic is, either. There's nothing wrong with getting along with who I get along with and it's not going to change. I like my personality fine. It has been this way for me socially and romantically my whole life and it's been challenging in the alienation sense, especially with the romantic piece, you know? Like, imagine you are my age and attempting conversations with other people your age and it's just not working. Differences in taste and frame of reference aside, what I've predominantly encountered in my peers is a literal incapacity for discourse. It's not a superiority thing. It's a "how the fuck can I function in this world" thing. It's just as much my incapacity, my defectiveness. For instance, that guy in the visor whipping his blonde hair back and forth, Bernard I think it was, who you had to take home in a drug haze the other night. Nice and cool and funny as I found him, I don't think you'd disagree that Bernard and I didn't really have much to say to one another, much in common, and I don't think there's any doubt or mystery about us being vastly different people (without making qualitative, character judgments about either of us) despite being (gasp!) closer in age than you or I, say. I don't think you'll be driving me home anytime soon. I won't be drooling in a stupor as you draw me a bath. Okay, so imagine now that you've been isolated for the longest and then you actually start meeting people you like and get along with and can talk freely to with candor, be vulnerable and show tender parts of yourself to, and they're older than you and they like and get along with you, too, and maybe some of them even have feelings for you, and they feel weird about it, so they tell you, they set boundaries, you know, the delineations of why these things don't work. The disclaimers, the qualifying, the hair-ruffling relegations to friendships. Imagine feeling like you've really glimpsed, seen a complex, challenging, and worthwhile individual, and they you. You start to feel that you could maybe care for him, and then the same shit. The tune you played me at the bar I recognized after hearing its first note. You gave me your unique rendition of it, but its melody is embedded. It wasn't hard to hear ultimately (I've grown to expect it), but what made me a little sad

was that you felt you had to say it, that I needed to hear it. That you had to nip it, whatever it was, in the bud. It just kind of made my insides sink lower than their usual sag. I'll always admit that I could be way off, thinking wishfully or projecting my hopes, but it felt like maybe you were stopping yourself, drawing that line for yourself, because you felt something, even if it was a small something, too. I stopped speculating what other people's motivations might be a long time ago, so I'll leave it at that. Whatever your motivation was, I believe it was genuine and from a place of giving a shit, and I appreciate you being forthright with me. And thank you for offering to be my friend. Apologies for sending this at this hour. Hopefully, you're asleep and this won't keep you up and you can just read it in the morning. I would have emailed you but I don't have your address.

He texted me back the next day

He told me it was the longest text he had ever received

That it was not crazy-seeming, but pretty reasonable

He told me he sometimes got himself into trouble for thoughtlessly saying hurtful things while drunk

He apologized

"Plus, I like spending time with you, so there"

Peaches flew up to get his things from storage and drive them down to New Orleans

Ryan was in D.C. visiting his brother and tying up loose ends

Peaches had expressed a lot of regret to me about breaking up, that maybe all that mattered *was* love

We slept in the same bed, but only had sex a couple times, and very briefly

We mostly just cuddled

It was sad—both the material and symbolic finality of it

I got out of the shower and Peaches was acting weird

I pressed him

He told me he unlocked my phone—I had told him the code once, and he had remembered it

He read my text history with Ryan

Some of the texts were about Peaches

Ryan checking in on me to see how I was doing as I helped my ex leave to start a new life without me

I told Peaches that Ryan was my friend

The next morning, he and I loaded the last of his things in his rental truck

His regret was palpable

We both cried really hard

He took a long time to finally leave

Seeing him drive away hurt so bad

He called me right after he turned the corner

I promised him I would always be a part of his life

He made me promise to be there if his mother died, or he was dying

I told him I loved him forever

I went back into my even emptier basement apartment

I cried, got drunk, talked to Joey on the phone, and went to sleep

Ryan texted me that he hooked up with a guy and his friend over Pride, and that the guy texted him that his friend tested positive for Gonorrhea

"I'm getting tested and treated—you should too, just in case"

Even though I had not had sex with him since Pride, I got tested and treated prophylactically, and got enrolled in a program to get PrEP (which had gained prominence during my time with Peaches) for free while I was at it

I met Ryan for coffee after

He had to get up during our talk to have the antibiotic runs

I asked him if he had ever been in a relationship

He told me he had not

"There's a cold stone with the word 'bitch' on it where my heart used to be"

He told me he had dated guys for a few months at the most, that he had gotten close to a relationship, but never committed

He told me he had moved to San Francisco when he was younger, and he wanted to fall in love, and have a boyfriend

He told me guys would shame him for wanting a boyfriend/ monogamy

He told me he changed his behavior to try to get guys to like him

He told me he had some bad experiences, that he was in some of the first PeP trials, some close calls

He told me he knew a guy who got gang-raped and then tested positive for HIV

He told me that once in a park he got aggressively sandwiched by two black guys trying to hold him down and he freaked out and pushed them off and ran away

I am telling you what he told me

He told me he was scared of HIV for the longest, that he and his friend used to joke about "AIDS all gone"—some miracle cure

And then PrEP came out, and the miracle was real, and he swore off condoms

I told him he had said and done things that gave me the impression he was looking for a boyfriend, including listing that in his Scruff profile as a possibility: "maybe even a boyfriend, too"

He had also been really affectionate to me

He agreed and said he was just affectionate like that, and that he was open to companionship, but that he took things slow, and his priorities right now were getting healthy and getting a job

He told me his friend told him you are never really ready to be in a relationship

He told me he was talking to his friend and told her I was, for my age and where I was in life, "doing all the right things"

He said his friend was coming into town that weekend and invited me to hang out with them

I was into it

SOMETHING GROSS

I looked forward to it

And he canceled, the sweet cherubic ginger bear

I did not text him for two days

"Okay, Ryan"

I told him I was crushed and asked if we could talk on the phone

He told me he did not want any drama

I told him I was not trying to create drama or conflict

"I know you're not trying to, but that's what's happening"

He told me he could only make tentative plans, the way that his life was right now

He told me that when he read the text that said I was crushed when he canceled plans, he thought "I can't give Ben what Ben wants"

He told me it seemed like I wanted a relationship, and he could not give that to me

I told him that I did not want that, at least not right now

He told me that it seemed like I did, and that was fine: "you do you"

I told him I could take things slow, and play it cool

I thanked him for "talking me off the ledge"—tentative plans were fine

He said he was glad we "deep lesbian processed" it

I laughed—that was a phrase he used often

Like "making bad decisions," "I'm on my last T cell," and "if I sneeze this whole room will get syphilis"

I was happy to be getting to know someone new

"When are we going to hang out again?"

It was Ryan's birthday

I met up with him and his friends at a drag show at Gladys

Ron, Chad, Jaime, and Paul Bee

Jaime was a big and hilarious Latino bear

He had a boyfriend named Andy

Paul was an old friend of Ryan's from his San Francisco days, visiting from Seattle—he had started a Bear circuit dance party several years ago, and it got big and went national

We quickly got bored of the drag show, so we went next door, to Trade

I told Ryan I had applied for a job at the R&R on East Colfax, that I had tended bar when I lived in Madison, before meeting Peaches and before school

"I can't imagine you bartending"

There was an afterparty at Ryan's apartment

I saw him over by the bathroom helping a younger guy put on a cock ring

"You can keep it—I got a bunch of 'em"

The younger guy went into Ryan's bedroom with Paul

I went over to see what all the action was about, peeking in

Ron was in there, too

Ryan and I went over and sat on the couch and snorted cocaine

"I'm gonna pop out on the balcony"

"Okay"

I met a guy, Pablo

He had a sharp, angular, groomed beard

"You're really cute, Ben"

He cupped my genitals, grinned, and looked at me with wide eyes

I did not say anything and backed away

"Hey, hey, relax—I'm just being friendly"

SOMETHING GROSS

I went out on the balcony

Ryan was talking to Chad, who was smoking a cigarette and chewing gum

"Hey, is that Pablo guy your friend?"

"Yeah, we hang out sometimes, why?"

"He was being pretty handsy"

"Oh, that's just Pablo"

We went back inside

The younger guy who had been in the room with Paul and Ron was in the living room in a jockstrap

He had two dark hickies in symmetrical locations on his clavicles

Apparently, Paul had roughed the whippersnapper up in a way that he wanted to be roughed up

Ron had been in a more bossy, voyeuristic, directorial role, Ryan and I were informed

Even though I had only known him for a few hours, it seemed a cautious assumption that Paul was a person who had a lot of sex

His career as a party promoter, indeed, was predicated on providing like-minded consumers a venue and forum where they could gain access to a variety of sex options and practices

And he moved freely in that world, traveling with his parties from city to city, hairy heinie to hairy heinie

Ryan and I snorted more cocaine

Everybody had left and it was just us

"Have you checked the mail today?"

"No—I saw a package for me . . . let me grab it"

He went downstairs and came back with a box containing a dozen yellow roses I ordered for him, including a note, which he read in front of me while sitting on the floor as I sat on the couch

The note told him the yellow roses symbolized friendship and piss, that I felt grateful to have met him, that he had been helping me through a difficult time, and that he was a wonderful, special person

"That's really nice—that's really, really nice"

He scooted over to me, emotion in his eyes and face

I got on the floor with him and held and kissed him

"I wasn't sure if you had anyone in your life to do stuff like this for you—make you feel cared for, so I wanted to"

"I don't—not anymore—thank you"

We put the yellow roses in a vase and he smelled them

"I love flowers, I used to get them for my mom—the note means the most, though"

He was wearing a t-shirt with an illustration of a man's head getting pissed on

We sat back down on the floor and he pulled a book out of a cabinet

It was a homemade artistic scrapbook from his college years that his friend put together

He showed me a picture of his young self, with long, curly, orange hair—he looked like a grunge kid

"Oh my God—look at you—what a cutie"

I turned the page—there was text on the back, a quotation attributed to Ryan, which I automatically read aloud

It was unexpectedly heavy, and my voice changed reading it as I realized its weight

It was about how a guy he dated took advantage of him

I don't know what's wrong with me. I can't separate sex and emotion. I loved him. He really hurt me.

"Oh my GOD—did you know this was in here?!"

"Whoa, no . . . I forgot"

"This is incredible, poor . . . how old were you?"

"Nineteen"

"—Poor nineteen-year-old you"

"Yeah, I really couldn't separate sex and emotion back then"

"Why do you think you've never been in a relationship—what are you scared of?"

"Being humiliated . . ."

"Yeah . . . there's always that risk—that happened to me"

"From what you've told me, Peaches seemed pretty normie-gay for you"

"Yeah, he'd drag me to things I didn't want to go to, but he could be wild"

"Can I see a picture of him"

I pulled up a picture on my phone and showed it to him

"He's cute"

"Yeah, I mean, he was my boyfriend"

"Not as cute as Ryan Bless"

He described himself as having a "radical queer aesthetic"

He had a framed Courtney Love concert poster, as well as a Wonder Woman poster, as well as a bunch of graphic t-shirts, the designs of which included Divine from the John Waters movies, Björk, and Christeene Vale

He told me about his father

"Feelings were bad in his household—he was really manipulative"

He told me he was worried his father would leave all his money to his brother when he died, and his brother would not give half to him—that he was not sure if he could talk to his brother again if he did not give him half

We stood and hugged and kissed in the middle of the living area

I pushed my nose and mouth into the side of his neck

"You smell really good"

He smelled me

"You smell good, too, in your sexy undershirt—you smell like my dad, actually"

"... Really?"

We had sex

Immediately after, he teared up

"Nobody's done that to me before, made me feel that way"

I told him I loved him

He hugged me

"I thought you were gonna tell me that"

In the morning, Paul came over

He was on his phone, promoting his parties on social media

It was decided that we would get bagels, then go to the Denver Swim Club, a bathhouse on East Colfax past the R&R, with Paul and Ron

We checked in at the DSC with the person behind the plexiglass—signed our waivers and paid our fees, received our locker keys and towels

Ryan requested an XL towel

"The ones they give you by default are small"

I asked for one as well

We took our clothes off and put them in our lockers, put towels around our waists and key coils around our arms

Ryan and I jumped in the pool together

He was on the swim team in high school and told me that's why he was attracted to guys who looked like me

"Did you ever swim?—you have the perfect body for it . . ."

"No, I'm not very good at swimming"

We kissed for a while, then I told him to get on my shoulders

I waded with him on top of me toward the deep end

"Okay—we're going to go under that lane thing"

I inhaled deeply and submerged myself, walking in a crouch under the plastic divider

Ryan got clotheslined and fell backwards—I surfaced excitedly

"Did it work?"

He and I went inside and got in the hot tub and started making out with his legs wrapped around me

"Ew, gross"

Ron interrupted us and got in the hot tub

Murals were covering the walls surrounding the indoor pool

Various sexually suggestive forms of sea life—a hammerhead shark, a jellyfish that looked like a penis draped in a translucent veil

An old fat guy floated over in the pool to the other side of the hot tub partition behind Ron

"Do you mind if I give you a back rub?"

"No thanks, I'm good"

We all looked at each other, then laughed after the guy floated away

Ron got out of the hot tub to explore

There was a TV with porn playing on it mounted in the corner of the pool room

Ryan and I watched a scene with two punk-looking guys that ended with one of them nutting in a skateboarding shoe

"What the fuck"

Ryan and I were cracking up

Paul got in the hot tub

"What're you lovebirds laughing about?"

Ryan rolled his eyes

"Weird porn"

We all showered and left, ate some pizza together at a restaurant in Capitol Hill

I said goodbye to them on the street, hugging Ryan and telling him I had a great time

Before I got in the car I ordered to Union Station, I yelled "byiiiiiieeeeeee" and Ryan laughed

Ryan visited me again in Boulder

We cuddled in the bed Peaches and I had slept in together for years

While I was making us sandwiches after, he came into the kitchen with a tiny pink book

A Shakespearean sonnet bathroom reader that Peaches had given me

He read one of the sonnets aloud, then looked at me awkwardly

"That didn't happen"

He ate his sandwich in his underwear across from me, in the booth Peaches had acquired from a closing restaurant in Memphis that he decided to leave behind

Ryan was a gorgeous bear

His skin was pale, smooth, and soft, with lots of freckles

I put on a song and lip-synched it to him while dancing

He was cracking up

He told me he liked how I was masculine, but could also be really gay

I got the job at the R&R—a small dive bar

The oldest active gay bar in Denver—used to be the poz bar back in the day

I told the owner that commuting from Boulder would not be an issue for me, that I was planning on moving to the city before it got too cold

I got back in the groove of tending bar before too long

Ryan came to visit me during a happy hour I was working

He flirted with me from across the bar

"This is nice, now I can come in here and make everyone jealous of me for having a hot bartender boyfriend"

He had not said the boyfriend word before, and it excited me

Ryan was going to Southern Decadence for Labor Day in New Orleans

While he was down there, I texted him the link to a poem of mine that got published on the internet

He said he enjoyed the poem, that it was honest, even showing it to a friend of his

It was a love poem

After he got back to Denver, we were hanging out one night and he told me he had missed me when he was down there

I told him if he ever missed me, he could tell me in the moment, that I would like to hear that, that I had missed him, too

I had not seen him in a week or so, and he texted me that even though he had only hooked up with one person over the weekend, that person had contacted him and told him he thought he had gonorrhea—"a shot, pills, and seven days of no thrills"

I was at Trade with Ryan and his friends, and this younger guy, Chason, mentioned having had a gonorrhea scare

Ryan asked me if he could talk to me—he told me he and Chason had fooled around, but were not serious—just friends

"Plus, I think he's crazier than you or I"

Later that night, we snorted a bunch of Cocaine at the bartender Evan's house

I knew Evan from when I lived in Wisconsin for a couple years in my early twenties, tending bar in Madison—he had tended bar in Milwaukee

Chason and a couple, Al and Steve, were there

Everybody ended up naked—nobody did anything, though

At one point, Ryan came over to me and whispered

"Hey I really want to suck Steve's dick, but I don't want to do it in front of you"

Chason asked Ryan if they could talk outside

Deep lesbian processing

Ryan came back in and I went outside to talk to Chason

He told me that he felt a really strong connection with Ryan, but Ryan didn't feel the same way

I told Chason I was sorry

"That's okay—maybe we could spit roast him to get over it"

Ryan was going back to D.C. again

The night before he left, he visited me at the R&R while I was closing

I told him I wanted to talk to him

He hung out while I closed, and drove me back to his apartment

"So things got a little weird the other night . . ."

He told me he wished I had not told him I loved him

"You don't always have to say what you feel"

He told me I had bad breath

I am telling you what he told me

I told him I had worked all night and had not had the chance to brush my teeth—I told him he could use the opportunity of his trip to D.C. to think about what he wanted

I was tending bar when I got a text from Ryan telling me he thought about it and that we should go our separate ways romantically and sexually and be friends, that he would be playing darts at the bar with Chad after I got off work if I wanted to talk about it

I counted out my drawer and was going to the bathroom before leaving out the back, and Ryan came in while I was washing my hands

"Hey, I just wanted to say I can talk about it if you want to"

I nodded, then left the bathroom

I turned around and went back in—Ryan was doing a bump in the stall

"Hey, that was shitty the way you told me that—you could have at least told me in person"

"Yeah, I'm sorry—I just thought because you were a writer, that was your preferred method—plus, you're a millennial—God, and I told you your breath smelled, sorry, that was rude"

Ryan had brought up the millennial/texting thing to me before

Texts, for him, he said, were informational bulletin boards that you responded to when you could, and that he found it mildly annoying to get texts that did not "have a point"

Meanwhile, he had what he referred to as a "drunken gay group text" he named after himself, "Bless's Messes," and used more emojis than anybody I had ever dated

It was alright—told him I could just come over and fuck him without emotional attachment if he wanted

"Okay . . ."

I went with Ryan and Chad to Trade

I felt terrible

I found them doing bumps in the bathroom

"Hey, I'm leaving"

"Oh, okay"

"Take care"

I hugged him quickly, left, and went back to Boulder

I could not sleep that night

I sent a long text to Ryan

> *I'm disappointed in myself for pathetically offering attachment-less sex as an option, to feel close to you. My case here is not special. I've run my course in one of your cycles. You've done this to others. It's not that you can't give me what I want, or in the manner you infantilized me over the phone, speaking of me, to me, a few months ago, "I can't give Ben what Ben wants." What I wanted was a basic standard of decency and consideration. When I held you accountable to that, you belittled me. You've belittled, demeaned, condescended to, and humiliated me. You lead me on. You said things to me you didn't mean so that I would have sex with you. You said you loved me back. It might have been attached to a bunch of "but"s, but you told me that. You're like the person your young self described in that book your friend put together that you showed me. You*

couldn't separate sex and emotion, you said. He used you for sex, you said. You loved him, you said. You've become what hurt you. You went through it, but you didn't get through it. I was blown away when you told me you'd jeopardize your relationship with your brother, who you like, if he didn't give you half your dad's money, who you hate, when he dies. That's so low in character, it's biblical, and unfathomable to me. I'm angry at myself for letting myself get drawn into you for so long. For empathizing with a person who took little effort to feel for me. Your priorities, you say, are getting healthy and getting a job. Your priorities, based on your actions, are partying and numbing yourself. You're in a drug and alcohol and sex-fueled grief spiral. You're a forty-four-year-old man, and you said to my face, a twenty-eight-year-old, that someone dating you gets in the way of achieving those priorities, it annoys you, even. It's not your fault. You've never been in a real thing before. You don't know what it takes, nor do you have what it takes, to really be there for another person. You have your thoughts and aspirations, the way you fancy yourself, and then there's what you actually do. Different worlds. If you wanted to get a job and get healthy, you'd do it. You might as well be a kid saying he wants to be an astronaut. There's no excuse for the way you've treated me. You've directly hurt me in a way I know I didn't deserve. So, you do you. Process it like a deep lesbian. Get those priorities straight. It's not someone who cares for you and wants to see you thrive and not wither, who's going to keep you from achieving what you say your goals are. It's snorting your inheritance regularly. It's going out and getting fucked and yakked up as soon as you feel better, so that you then feel horrible for the next day(s), and you flake on the person who's trying to pull you out of your shit, and you flake on yourself. That's what they don't tell you: that when you flake on others, you flake on yourself. You told me you wished I wouldn't have told you I loved you. You said, "you don't always have to say what you feel." Think about that. You said that to me. As if I didn't know that was technically true, that I didn't always have to say what I felt. As if I didn't deliberate and worry over telling you that for weeks. I'm not blaming you for being fucked up and terrified of any expression of intimacy beyond "I want to breed your hole" and "I want to piss on you" being said by a group of men you've arranged. God forbid I kink shame. But I take issue with you making like you were opening up, even suggesting, in some sly, sick way, that I was your boyfriend. I feel utterly manipulated and used, emotionally and mentally, and it's my fault for letting such a weak person make me feel needy for wanting such basic human things. You're not in a place to talk to me about anything that happens between people. You seem to be incapable of taking ownership of your actions or feeling remorse for those you hurt. I've earned this all, telling you what I feel. I will tell you what I feel. I'm not afraid of it. You have work to do. Don't waste time. It is so precious.

I sent Joey what I sent Ryan

"Holy shit"

He told me sending Ryan such a thing, after a certain point, ceased to be about Ryan, but was something I was doing for myself

"Like, you're saying 'this is how little you mean to me, that I'm gonna just shit all over you'"

I told Swayze, a regular at the R&R, what happened

"Oh, you were dating *her*?—I'd have warned you if I'd known"

He told me that maybe Ryan would face himself, take responsibility, on his deathbed

I felt terrible for saying those things to him

I hugged my coworker in the backroom and cried about it

I saw Ryan after getting off work at the bar a week after I sent him the text

He threw darts three feet from my head without looking at me

Chad told me he was showing him the text and saying "I don't understand why"

I went to this older guy's apartment in Capitol Hill—close to Ryan's

I had been drinking at Trade and left to fuck him, then returned to Trade and got wasted

It was motorcycle night

I rode with a daddy bear on the back of his three-wheeler thirty minutes to his home in Lafayette

He sucked my dick in his lukewarm jacuzzi and I passed out

I woke between him and his husband, who I noticed had a prosthetic hand/arm—they were both wearing CPAP masks

I was tending bar and Chad came in and mentioned Ryan had gone to the emergency room because he thought he was having a heart attack, but he was fine

It had been in the morning after lots of alcohol/cocaine

I moved to Denver on Halloween

I took some Xanax and drank and threw up in the back of the R&R

I hooked up with a minor bear-lebrity when he was in town doing stand-up comedy

I went to Wisconsin for Thanksgiving—she seemed worse

Ryan and I made up

I canceled Peaches's trip to see me, hurting him horribly

Ryan tried to have a "sober January" and made it a week

We went on a date

"I don't want to freak you out, Ben, but I think I'm falling in love with you"

I was in love with him

I told Swayze at the R&R what happened

"Remember—tigers don't change their stripes—and that means you too kid, and what you want"

My coworker got fired and went to rehab in Utah on his parents' money

I got fired and drank at Trade

The Time Ryan Gave Me Antibiotic-Resistant Gonorrhea

Ryan and I were walking at Cheesman in the snow

Satisfyingly crunching through the upper icy layer of it and down into the grass

He expressed how it was annoying and making it hard to walk

I started stepping carefully so I did not break through

I smiled

"That's weird, it's only happening for you"

Ryan's dimples formed and he rolled his eyes

"Oh right, because I'm fat"

"Yes—that was the joke I was making—that you are fat"

Ryan was dropping me off at Tyrone's house, where I was renting a room

He drove me home after lunch

We were supposed to hang out all day, but he told me he was not feeling up for it

We were parked out front, and I turned to him

"Can I tell you something?"

"Sure—what's up?"

"I feel you really reaching out to me, like 'love me!—love me!'— and I move to come in, and you put the wall up—it's like some bait and switch shit"

He sighed, looking at me sadly

"It's not often that someone tells me something about myself that I don't already know, but you're right"

"I thought we were going to keep hanging out"

"My stomach is upset and I knew you were going to want to have sex"

"I don't need to have sex with you every time we hang out, Ryan—I love spending time with you"

We went back to his place, cuddled and watched a movie

Falling asleep together, I was telling him about my visit to Wisconsin over Thanksgiving, and how my mother was masking her symptoms

"I wanted to tell her 'you don't have to—it's okay—I know'"

I started crying and so did he

"Hey Ben . . ."

Ryan woke me

He was standing at the edge of the bed in his underwear

He was crying

"Oh, oh, oh—come here"

I held him as he shook

"I couldn't sleep, so I started to clean—I saw a picture of my mom on the shelf and started crying"

BIG BRUISER DOPE BOY

He calmed down

We talked about his mother

He told me how he showed to his mother's house once and she was covered in shit and there was shit all over the place

"I was like, 'my mom's crazy'"

He told me she screamed at him waiting in line at the grocery store

"I—want—grandchildren!"

He told me her sense of humor got weird as she declined

He told me she was religious, and in the dismay of her diagnosis told him she had "done everything right"

He told me she once asked him if he believed in God

He told me he wanted to tell her "I don't fucking care"

He told me she had been his "best friend"

I did not relate

My mother had never been my best friend

My mother was my mother

He told me to get my mother in a home sooner rather than later, while she could still adjust to it

My writer friend George was over at Tyrone's

I had met George on Twitter when I lived in Boulder, and we realized we lived a mile away from each other

We were getting really stoned on cannabis concentrate using one of his many portable mods

I was on a video call with Leslie, George at my side

She, along with her husband Connor, were publishing my first book on Valentine's Day

She was drinking wine

"If you were straight, we'd fuck, because you're hot, and I'm hot—every hot male writer wants to fuck me"

I looked at the thumbnail feed of myself and George in the upper-left corner of the call and saw him slowly leave the frame

I could hear Connor say something from the bedroom—she was being loud and he was trying to sleep

She told me they were setting up readings in Denver for me and other writers in the area

I told her to get my boy George on the lineups

We ended the call

"Dude, that was so awkward"

"Yeah man, this is who is putting out my book—can you imagine if I were a straight guy and I said some shit like that to a lesbian?"

"She was so drunk—Connor . . . fuck"

"I wonder if he's like . . . into getting cucked"

I had shared my excitement about the book with Ryan

I had a reading in Boulder next month, too

He seemed excited for me, while also telling me a career in art might not work out

He told me he was not trying to be discouraging, just realistic

I was not discouraged—I was determined to do whatever I had to do to be able to continue to do what I was doing

I told him my friend Norm Black helped and encouraged me to get the book published

He texted me a picture of Norm

"I just looked him up—you guys could be brothers!"

I texted Norm a picture I had taken of Ryan in his underwear on the couch—his big legs on display

"Daaaaaamn—ask him if he has a thicc older sister"

I told Ryan what Norm said

"Not an older sister—just a scrawny younger brother!"

He was going on a gay bear cruise that Paul was hosting, a week-long Caribbean voyage embarking from PortMiami, getting back the Sunday before my book release

The night before he flew to Florida, I went over to his apartment

We were going out to dinner for his friend's birthday and he asked me to come over beforehand to help him apply Nair to his back

For smooth cruising

"Make sure to glop it on real thick, like cake batter"

I put a liberal layer of it on

"Can you smell that—the hair burning?"

"Yeah"

We let it sit on his back for the time indicated on the bottle, then wiped it away with towels that he decided to throw away instead of washing

"Thanks for the 'friend favor'—I owe you something gross"

He sucked my dick

After dinner, I told him I wanted to be his boyfriend, eventually

I was hanging out with Jaime, watching Drag Race at Zangief and Bernard's

Ryan had hooked up with Bernard a few times, he said, and then stopped when he found out he was with Zangief

He told me he brought it up to Zangief, telling him he didn't know they were together, and he told me Zangief told him it was okay

Jaime and I were eating cake in the kitchen

I told him about a text Ryan had sent me from the boat, telling me that the cruise lifestyle was not for him, and that he had not hooked up with anybody

He called me "babe" in the text

Other things he had called me: "mister"; "handsome"; "sexy"

"I miss him"

"Me too"

He was getting back in a couple days

Jaime texted him a video of me eating an entire piece of cake in one bite

"OMG—miss you bitch"

I was at Trade with Ryan and the bitches

He had gotten back that evening

Everybody was happy to see him

He grabbed my arm

"Hey, I have something to tell you—it's not a big deal or anything"

We left the group and he told me he hooked up with a guy the last night of the cruise

"It just kind of fell into my lap—he was at dinner with Paul and me"

I told him that it was okay, that I had hooked up with someone while he was gone

"Okay, cool—wanna see a picture of him?—he was this black guy with a nine-inch dick"

I am telling you what he told me

"Uh, sure"

He showed me the picture of the man with whom he had sex on the balcony of his room on the ship

It was odd—Ryan would complain about how racist his father was, and he said "I think everyone should have white privilege" more than once, as if he was right and good for saying it

It all struck me as fallacy, both ironic and absurd

Absurd, because the Eurocentric construct of whiteness—the colonial economy—required enslavement/exploitation

SOMETHING GROSS

That was like saying "I think everyone should have servants"

Ironic, because Ryan took no issue with himself fetishizing black men's bodies and their BBCs

What a D.C. cunt

We had sex that night—it was great to see him

I was spending the night at George's, outside Boulder

I was worried I had gonorrhea

I kept checking myself in the bathroom

I seemed to be urinating more than usual

I asked George to give me a ride to the clinic in the morning

The STD clinician came back and told me my sample showed an infection under the microscope

I got treated and texted Ryan

"Hey—thanks for letting me know—I have an appointment with my primary care physician this week, so I'll just take care of it then"

I texted the guy I hooked up with while Ryan was on the cruise

He texted me when he got his results back and told me they were negative

On Valentine's Day, I went over to Ryan's

We were celebrating our newfound love, as well as the release day of my book, which Connor told me would become a "cult success," that I was "like, the rebel"

I did not want to be a cult success or the rebel

I wanted a boyfriend

I got to Ryan's place and he gave me a gift bag with superheroes on it

Inside were chocolates and probiotic supplements

I had to repopulate my intestinal flora after being on antibiotics

He told me he got them at the grocery store, and thought of getting me flowers, but decided not to because I was coming over there, and he did not want to make me travel with flowers back to my place

"When are you going to let me see your place, by the way?"

"Not yet—it's a pigsty"

I still had most of my things from Boulder in boxes in the corner of my room at Tyrone's, using them as tables

I told him I had gotten a follow-up phone call from the clinic, and that the strain of gonorrhea I had was resistant to antibiotics, but that it was not "super gonorrhea," as it was only resistant to one of the two drugs with which I was treated

I told him the clinician told me the resistant strains often came to the country's interior from the coasts, and that he had given it to me

He said that was not necessarily true, that I could have gotten it from the guy I hooked up with while he was gone

I told him the person I hooked up with while he was gone had tested negative, which meant that he had given it to me, and the guy who fucked him on the cruise had given it to him

He owed me something gross, and he paid me back

"Oh, damn—well, thanks, Leon . . ."

I told him I was worried about it being resistant

He told me it was fine

I brought up the gonorrhea a few more times, once jokingly, and Ryan confronted me about it, telling me it was annoying him

"Do you think I'm supposed to feel bad about it?"

"No ..."

"Then why did you keep bringing it up?"

"I don't know—I'm sorry—you don't have anything to feel bad about"

"I know I don't have anything to feel bad about—I'm just wondering what's going on"

"I'm sorry—I'm just anxious about it"

"I used to worry about this sort of thing, but I'm gay—it's an occupational hazard—I just do what the doctor tells me to do"

We cooled off

We ordered food and watched a movie

We got in bed and kissed and cuddled

Ryan still had a bandage on his shoulder from his clap shot earlier that day

He told me it was the best Valentine's Day he had ever had

We told each other we loved each other

He told me he was worried I was using him as a "rebound," as the security after a breakup during a transition in my life

I told him I was not doing that

He asked me if Peaches and I told each other we loved each other a lot

"Yeah—all the time"

We were hanging out a week later

We made stir-fry

Smiling across from me above his empty plate, he told me how great it was to have dinner together

"You can come over here and do this with me—I can get the groceries—I know you need to save money right now while you're looking for another job"

Ryan needed a job, too

He had been unemployed for almost three years, and his savings/
trust fund were dwindling

He had a couple leads, though, in the nonprofit sector

He told me he was worried that if he did not get his shit together,
he would have to ask his friend if he could move in with her

His old friend with two children, whom he babysat sometimes

"Those kids get all my love"

He told me they called him "Uncle Pookie"

He asked me to sit with him on the couch

He told me the night after Valentine's Day, he had gotten fucked
by two guys at a house party he and Chad went to

Bareback, both of them

He told me one of them was waiting for him naked in the
bathroom, that he was really drunk and high on cocaine

"But you got treated for gonorrhea the day before, you're supposed
to wait, you—"

"—I know, I put those guys at risk"

"Did you tell them?"

"I told one of them and he was like 'whatever, it's probably fine' and I didn't have the other guy's number, so I couldn't get in touch with him"

"Fuck, Ryan"

"I know, I'm sorry, I feel like I'm out of control—I waited to tell you after dinner, because it was so nice, and I really like you—I love you—and I feel like I just fucked everything up"

He told me he had forgotten about getting treated the day before because he was so drunk and high, that he woke in the morning and "was like 'fuck'"

"I did this once before, when I lived in San Francisco"

He told me that two nights ago, he brought a guy home from a music show he attended with the Messes, and that they had sex

"I know it's not wrong on its own that I had sex with any of those guys—I just wanted to let you know"

He was right about that—we were not exclusive—we were dating, but it was disturbing to me that he had forgotten getting treated the day before, and that he had not told me about it sooner

"Why did you wait to tell me?"

"I wasn't ready"

"You knew it would hurt me, and you did it anyway"

I did not ask him about the third guy—what was a third on day seven after two on day one?

He had unprotected sex with three guys in a seven-day window during which he knew he was not supposed to have sex

He was supposed to do what the doctor told him to do

It was day eight—I had been looking forward to having sex with him

"You couldn't wait a goddamn week!"

"I know—I'm sorry!"

"How many times have you had gonorrhea?"

"I dunno— a lot?!"

We cooled off and went to Zangief and Bernard's to watch Drag Race

I called Joey and told him what happened

"He forgot?!"

"That's what he told me"

"Yeah, that's not forgetfulness—that's called 'not giving a fuck about anyone but yourself'"

I texted Ryan

"Did you tell Mandingo he gave you the superclap?"

"Ummm . . . 'Mandingo'?"

I told him Mandingo was the name of a porn star—a black man with a very large penis

"Gotcha—yeah, I let him know"

He was fine objectifying black guys—he just could not have the fact that he did it named to him

He was a D.C. cunt

Thanks, Leon

Hips and I were hanging out in his "rich white lady car"

His mother had given it to him, and she was, well, see above

He had been an R&R regular who developed a crush on me that I redirected into a friendship

He had also been having problems with "the mensisizz"

He and I would get together and commiserate

We had just retrieved his chess set from his ex's apartment

"Why do they do it to us, Ben?"

"I don't know, man"

"You know you're going to keep getting STDs if you keep sleeping with him, right?"

"Yeah, I know—he calls it an 'occupational hazard' of being a gay man . . . it's only an occupational hazard if your job is being a slut"

"Condoms still exist—I've never had gonorrhea—just the big one—made a stupid choice and won the fucking lottery"

I texted Ryan and told him how what he did was so reckless and irresponsible, that I did not know if I could trust him to not hurt me like that again

He agreed it was reckless and irresponsible, apologized, and told me he was not sure if he could not hurt me like that again, so we should talk

We met at a bar on Colorado Boulevard off a bus route that picked up near Tyrone's

I spoke first and told him everything was fine, that it hurt, but I would get over it, and I wanted to keep hanging out like we had been

"Okay, because this is me, Ben"

"It's okay—I kinda like it—you're wild and untameable"

"If at any point you feel like you can't do this anymore, it's okay"

"I feel like you're counting on that"

"I'm not"

We went to the bathroom to do bumps

We went back to his apartment and had sex

In the morning, we were kissing and cuddling

"I gotta piss—be right back"

On my way out of his room, I tucked my dick and balls between my legs, then bent down and showed him the "fruit basket"

He squealed and bent his knees

"Hey, do you hear something?"

I knew this by now as the setup to him farting

He farted, but it sounded wet

A foul burbling

He slammed his hands down at his sides, enclosing himself with the duvet

"Get out"

When I came back, he told me it had just been my cum from the night before

I called Joey and told him what happened, that I was going to try to make it work with Ryan, that we could try to help each other get better

"Jesus Christ—you sound like a battered housewife—your story about this guy keeps changing"

146

SOMETHING GROSS

It was my first reading for my first book, in Boulder

Hips gave me a ride

We met Ryan and Chad at a bar beforehand

Ron came down, too

It was touching that Ryan's friends came to my reading

"I hope they didn't feel obligated to come—did you tell them to?"

"No, this was all them—they wanted to come and support you—
they think it's cool"

I kept going to the bathroom to check myself for discharge

I had a panic attack while reading

I had to sit down halfway through due to my legs going numb

Sweat was falling from my face onto the pages

The people seemed to have an experience—laughing a lot and then
getting really quiet

When I finished and thanked everybody for coming, then stood and walked away from the reading corner, Ryan put his hand on my arm as I passed his chair

It felt really good

Like I could feel that he cared about me and was proud of me

I rode back to Denver with Hips, because Ryan and Chad wanted to get cocaine

In the car, he told me my disdain for Ryan was transparent

"You could try to hide it a little more"

We met Ryan and Chad at Trade

Ryan asked what had been going on with me before and during the reading

"You looked pretty rough"

I told him I had bad anxiety, that I had felt extra pressure with his friends there

I asked him if we could share all our kinks with each other (he had mentioned not fully disclosing his to me and that he would eventually) when we were alone later at his place

He told me we could

He was drunkenly sprawled on the carpet of his living area, leaning back on me as I sat on the couch, hugging him from behind

He told me about watersports, which I knew about

"Chad said you let him piss on you while he filmed it"

"He told you about that, huh?—we dated back when I was living here going to grad school, believe it or not—he looked a lot different then"

There was the cock and ball torture stuff, which I knew less about

He told me he had a guy come over a few weeks ago and insert needles in his testicles, his most violent session yet, the guy jabbing repeatedly

He told me he was squirming in pain

"Was it too much?"

"No, I loved it—that's what scared me—I felt crazy—it was like I was delighting in my own self-destruction"

He told me he told his friend, and his friend told him it sounded like he had a death wish

"Your balls, Ryan—you need those"

"Sometimes I think I do have a death wish and I just want to be dead like my mom"

I am telling you what he told me

He told me he wanted to show me all the CBT pictures on his phone sometime, a gallery of his genitals compromised by various forms of anguish, and then delete them all

He told me he had an "escort fetish"—that he mostly just browsed online profiles

"Have you ever paid for sex?"

" . . . Yes"

He told me he had been taking Viagra since he was twenty, ever since he had those bad experiences with that guy that took advantage of him, and that was why he never came in front of me, that he had problems getting and staying hard when another man was present

"That's my shit, Ben—have I scared you off?"

"No"

I kissed the top of his bald head and its surrounding ring of stubble

"So, what are your deep, dark, fucked up kinks?"

"Oh . . . I, uh . . . I like daddy/son stuff"

"I mean, I kind of figured that about you already—is that it?"

"Yeah"

I made him get in the bathtub so I could piss on him

I told my friend Layla what Ryan told me

I told her about his and my dynamic

She told me about "attachment styles"

She told me he was an island and I was a wave

Sounded right to me

I asked her for therapist recommendations for Ryan, and she recommended her teacher, Emmett

He specialized in abuse/trauma and compulsive/out of control sexual behavior

Seemed like a good fit for Ryan

I texted him Emmett's info/website

I told him Layla told me he was an island and I was a wave

He told me that sounded right to him

He thanked me

He sent Emmett an email and started seeing him every week

I brought a bottle of sparkling rosé and a big chocolate chip cookie to Ryan's

He had just completed his first job interview in years—a video call

I wanted to show him how proud I was of him

I poured the bubbly from the bottle into his mouth as he knelt

I pissed in his mouth

He sucked my dick until I came

I ate most of the cookie I brought for him because he did not want it

I asked how his appointments with Emmett were going

He told me they were going well

He told me they talked about me, that Emmett challenged him

"So, based on what you've told me about Ben—you like him because he's hot"

Ryan asked me if I had seen the picture of Emmett on his website

I told him I had

He told me Emmett was not good-looking, and therefore did not understand

I am telling you what he told me

He dismissed his therapist's critique of him being superficial by insulting his looks

What else should I have expected from a D.C. cunt?

"Oh, and he told me you're an island and I'm a wave"

"Wait—I told you that—you don't remember that?"

"No . . . you did?"

"Yeah girl, we had a whole deep conversation about it"

"Must be my alcohol-induced dementia"

We went out to eat with Ron and Jaime before going over to Zangief and Bernard's to watch Drag Race

I got back from the bathroom, and after sitting in the booth, Ryan told me he told them about the rosé, the piss, and the jism

I was being very affectionate with him, sitting close as we ate and periodically hugging his side and rubbing him

When Chad drove us to Trade after Drag Race, I sat behind Ryan and kept touching his neck and shoulders

He told me to stop

It was Ryan, Chad, Jaime, and I back at Ryan's after the bar

Doing lines

Ryan told us about his mother working at a grocery store during the early stages of her Alzheimer's

"She had to leave after a while because she couldn't understand numbers"

SOMETHING GROSS

I told him my mother could not comprehend the value of numerals, either, anymore

Chad chimed in, attempting a silly face and voice

"Yeah, she was like 'is this fifty dollars or five?!'"

I laughed, shocked

"Oh my God—CHAD!"

Later, when we were alone, I brought up Chad making fun of his mother

"That's Chad—I'm pretty sure he's on the spectrum"

He told me to wait where I was until he called me into the bedroom

I found him on his hands and knees in a jockstrap

"I don't want you to touch my dick—just use my ass"

I grabbed the band of his jockstrap and kissed the birthmark above his crack

"Fucking use me"

I "used" him

"Oh, fuck yeah, Ben—shred my hole"

Cuddling after, he told me I had a "perfect penis"

"It's got a huge head—I can feel the edge of it dragging along inside me when you pull out—it's like a prison rapist cock"

I am telling you what he told me

I met Ryan at Trade for the Saturday beer bust

I had someone take a picture of us together

A guy named Lenny approached Ryan, joking with him about the last time they hung out

I did not understand what he was talking about

After the guy left, Ryan suggested I must sometimes feel like Eugene Levy's character in "Best in Show," who is married to Catherine O'Hara's character, and is present while different guys approach her throughout the movie, bringing up her promiscuous past

I then understood what that guy had been talking about

We left and got pizza near his apartment

SOMETHING GROSS

On the way up his building's stairs, I referred to something

"You know about all this obscure art—it's hard to keep up"

He told me to sit on the couch with him

"I don't want to do this anymore, Ben"

"What?"

"Something's changed"

He told me he did not want to date anymore/be boyfriends/continue "doing whatever it is we've been doing"

I started to cry

He asked me what was going on with me the other night—why had I been so handsy?—his friends had noticed

"I don't know—I wanted to touch you—I guess maybe I felt this coming"

"I can see that"

I told him I had thought we were going to have a nice night together

I told him I wanted to move back to Wisconsin

"Yeah—what's keeping you here, Ben?"

I had thought he was keeping me there

I told him I had thought we were going to have a nice night together

"You've said that four times already"

He told me he was relieved

I am telling you what he told me

He asked if I was going to be okay to go over to Evan's house

He had been planning to go over there for cocaine

I told him I would be okay

We walked to Evan's

Lenny was there with his husband, Wyatt

They were both teasing Ryan about breaking their toilet

Ryan told them now was not the time

I realized they were referring to the night after Valentine's Day

I tried to make a joke

"That's Ryan—always breaking toilets!"

A few weeks ago, Ryan had accidentally flushed a small bottle of lube down the toilet and clogged it—he ended up having to buy a new toilet and have it installed

We all got blasted on cocaine

I told Ryan I wanted to go back to his place after and talk

Ryan and I walked back to his apartment

I told him he wanted to have a boyfriend, but did not want to *be* a boyfriend

I told him to take that shit off his Scruff profile

I ordered a car, and when I walked out the door, I felt his hand on my lower back

It felt terrible

Jim met me at Cheesman

He had started as an R&R regular and became a good friend

We had bonded over literature, music, and hating people

Also, we drank and did cocaine together

He worked on the phone for the state, helping get medication for people who were living with HIV

He used to be a sales executive at an insurance company, making six figures

His department got purged

He "crashed the plane" after that, but he could sleep at night knowing he was serving people in need

He worked nights at Ross

I loved him

I cried to him about Ryan, and he listened

I went to The Denver Triangle with Hips

Jaime was there with a group of friends

SOMETHING GROSS

He saw me and made a sad face

"Hey boo—I heard—I'm sorry—but at least we can finally have sex now!"

I texted Ryan pleading with him to reconsider, and he told me he had already said to me everything he wanted to say, and that he hoped we could be friends

I told him he was an addict

He blocked my phone number and social media accounts

I got lunch with Dutch at the mall downtown

He was Evan's downstairs roommate

He told me Ryan had come over the other night, a weeknight, for cocaine

He told me he eavesdropped on their conversation, sitting on the stairs, and that Ryan was talking about having broken up with me

He told me he sounded relieved

I was at Tyrone's, boiling frozen potstickers from the Asian grocery store down the block

He now had a throuple renting a space in his backyard for their trailer, using water and electricity from the house

Probably illegal

Definitely annoying

Fucking slumlord

He had also come onto our straight roommate when he was drunk, multiple times

I did not like Tyrone

Neither did the older woman he paid to clean his house every other week

Mary

She would talk shit about him to me while she was cleaning and he was gone

She told me he had repeatedly tried to stiff/short her, or pay her late, once while in the same day showing her new clothes he had just bought

She told me she could not be friends with a person she did not respect

Tyrone entered the kitchen, coughing histrionically

"Are you cooking something?"

"You mean here, in the kitchen?—yeah"

I was walking to Carl's Jr. one morning

I noticed a bunch of puppies running around in a yard a few houses from Tyrone's

A woman with a buzzcut and a nasal cannula greeted me

She introduced herself as Scorpio

We had a great conversation

I told her I was doing a poetry reading that week at Mutiny Cafe, if she was by chance into "radical queer poetry"

I thought she might be a lesbian, so I put that out there, because I looked like a neo-Nazi, if not just a scary guy, I had been told before

The only thing radical about me was that I cared about what I wrote

BIG BRUISER DOPE BOY

The only thing queer about me was that I hated groups of gay people

She told me she could probably make it to the reading, and so could her husband

The reading went great—no nerves like last time—no pressure—I was alone

Scorpio and her husband Lad came up to me after the reading

They told me I was their favorite of all the readers, which included a woman who looped electric violin riffs

They told me they were looking for a roommate

I told them I was looking for a room

After the reading, I called Joey

"How'd it go?"

"No panic attack"

"Awesome"

"Guess who sponsored the reading?"

"Who?"

"Meow Wolf"

"Oh weird, that was that place in Santa Fe we didn't go to, right?"

"Yeah"

"Miss you"

"Miss you, too"

Also at the reading were Brentford and his DJ friend Zac

I had met Brentford at the R&R

He was a daytime regular, an insufferable drunk

But he was dry now

He filmed the reading for me

Zac told me he dug my stuff

I was walking into Tyrone's and he was eating takeout on his bed with the door open

"Hey—is this you—'Big Bruiser . . . Dope . . . Boy'?"

He handed me a package along with some mail

"Oh, yeah, that's me"

I noticed a letter from my father in the stack

I looked at his name, then mine

Ben Gross
[XXXX] N. Jackson St.
Denver, CO [XXXXX]

I had not seen him in over a decade

The letter told me he would be in town, and he wanted to get together

Sure, fuck it, I forgave him every day—why not do it in person?

Brentford became my friend

He "employed" me (paid me to hang out with him at his rented office space while he brainstormed)

He wanted to help me out—he knew I was in a rough spot

He had grand ideas that did not make a lot of sense

He was all over the place and could not commit to anything

He told me Zac was starting a new bear bar with his friends

He told me he could get me a job

He introduced me to the owners and I was hired the next day

The bar was not open yet—I was hired to help get the space ready

I worked with Zac six days a week for two months, building a DJ booth he designed, among myriad other tasks

We bonded—he was awesome

The first to acknowledge his "Scottish temper"

He looked like if Gandalf went to Burning Man

Peaches was visiting me

He had lost trust in me because I had lied to him about my feelings for Ryan

I had strung him along

I loved two men at the same time, but was only *in* love with one

Peaches and I walked around the city together

I showed him the bear bar in progress

We went to Trade to watch Drag Race

Ryan showed

"Oh shit"

"He's here, isn't he?"

"Yep—damnit, I thought he was going to watch Drag Race at Zangief and Bernard's"

Peaches did not know what Ryan looked like, though he imagined murdering him if they ever met

He had it planned—what he was going to say to Ryan before making him bleed out

"So, you're the guy who used my ex-boyfriend's mother's illness to emotionally manipulate him and take him from me"

We watched the queens lip-sync for their lives to a Demi Lovato song

Baby, I'm sorry (I'm not sorry)
Baby, I'm sorry (I'm not sorry)
Bein' so bad got me feelin' so good
Showin' you up like I knew that I would
Baby, I'm sorry (I'm not sorry)
Baby, I'm sorry (I'm not sorry)
Feelin' inspired 'cause the tables have turned
Yeah, I'm on fire and I know that it burns

I made us leave after, walking directly past Ryan without looking at him

After Peaches had left, Ryan approached me at Trade one evening, putting his hand on my back

He asked me to talk

I told him it hurt really bad to see him out

He told me he had blocked me across the board electronically, that I had been nasty in my texts to him

He told me he had thought he felt one way, and then he did not

He told me he thought I probably thought that was bullshit, and that he had gotten scared

169

I asked him to unblock me

He told me he was not ready

"I can't, Ben—I have to protect my feelings from you cutting into me—this might sound condescending, but has anyone ever told you that you hide behind words?"

"My mom told me that once"

"It's the best and worst thing about you—I like *this* Ben, the in-person Ben"

I told him how humiliating his breaking up with me was, how he inflicted his worst fear on me

I told him I got a letter from my father, and that I was going to confront him

He told me we could talk about that

We hugged

I talked to Ron after

"Ryan and I met each other during really fucked up times in our lives"

SOMETHING GROSS

Jaime and I started hanging out more, hitting it off as friends

We would get stoned and make each other laugh

When Ryan and I were not talking the first time, Jaime's boyfriend Andy beat him up, and Jaime had taken out a restraining order against him

Ryan drove Jaime to the court for the hearing

Andy went to anger management classes, and the order was lifted

They were cool now

Jaime and I went to Trade and saw Ryan and Chad there

Jaime was wearing a shirt my friend had designed and printed, with my pen name on it

Ryan pointed at him and said "get away from me"

Ryan asked me if the jeans I was wearing were new

I told him they were not

"Okay, Ben, fine—I'll stop looking at your bulge"

Jaime and I went to a warehouse rave

Ryan and Chad showed soon after

Ryan was drunk

He was helping young people tap a keg and Chad was talking to me

"Ryan's Gen X—he's a problem solver—everything always has to be his idea, though—things always have to be on his terms"

Ryan told me a few weeks ago that Chad told him he was in love with him, and always had been

I told him he was using Chad for drugs

He did not disagree

Chad was Ryan's age

He lived at his parents' house and received an allowance

He had a meth phase a decade ago, and had been living with HIV for a while

Ryan and I were waiting in line to do bumps in the bathroom and a guy approached me

"Hey, did you do a reading in Boulder a little while ago?"

Ryan and I looked at each other, smiling with mouths open

"Yeah, I did"

"I thought that was you—I just wanted to tell you how much I loved it"

"Wow, thanks a lot, man—I really appreciate it"

Ryan turned to me

"I bet that's never happened to you before"

"Nope"

He leaned in close and clutched my arm

I was wearing a muscle shirt

He told me how sexy I looked in it

We went to the bathroom and did bumps

I kissed him in the stall

He did not stop me

I ended up hanging out with Ryan another night

He still had me blocked, but we ran into each other and went to another bar together

"Let's go back to my place and eat leftover pizza and talk"

At his place, he told me how he liked this particular brand of frozen pizza

"The crust is really bready and doughy"

He told me while dating me, he responded to my emotional intensity, that I seemed really into him, and if someone felt that way about him, he should give it a try

"You told me you loved me multiple times"

"I know"

"Well, I'm so glad I could offer my heart to you as a trial ground for your failed romantic experiment"

"Ouch"

SOMETHING GROSS

He sat on the couch

I told him I was going to lay on the floor

He told me not to lay on the floor, holding his arms out

We cuddled

I lifted his face by his chin to kiss me

He resisted, then we started making out

After a while, I stood and held out my hands for his to hold mine—my "let's go to the bedroom" signal

"Nooo Ben—we can't have sex"

"We don't have to—I just want to cuddle"

"You know where that'll lead—you'll end up fucking me and we'll be staring deeply into each other's eyes"

I do not know why I ever thought he was scared of intimacy

He unblocked my number and told me we could get brunch sometime after he got back from D.C., where he was going to take care of something with his driver's license

Cunt

The bear bar, Honey, had its grand opening on Memorial Day weekend

I made a bunch of money

Ryan saw me scrambling around the upstairs patio during a barbacking shift

He told me I seemed really stressed

We decided to get brunch the following week, to try to "stumble our way through being friends"

Like Mary, I could not be friends with a person I did not respect, but I was going to try

Ryan picked me up from Tyrone's and we went to brunch at a place called Syrup—his choice

The kind of place with praline bacon

The kind of place with a dozen zany/chic varieties of pancakes

The kind of place I hated

He told me he had been hired by a nonprofit

I congratulated him

He told me he was concerned he might end up getting fired because he partied too much

I asked him how his trip home to D.C. went

He told me it went well, that he and his brother worked through some stuff

He told me his brother told him he was the most selfish person he knew

"You wanna give me the play-by-play with your dad?"

I told him what happened

I told him I emailed my stepsister

I told him she told me she wished I could have known my father the way she knew him, that he was a great man—kind, funny, caring, present—a great parent to her and her sisters

"This motherfucker broke my heart when I was FIVE YEARS OLD"

I told him I wanted to tell her I wished I could have known that person she knew, too, how that would have been so nice, but that it was better this way, and that I was glad my father was able to be a parent to *somebody's* children, if not his own flesh and blood

"Jeez—I wonder why I fall in love with older men who can't love me back"

He laughed, cringing and closing his eyes

Driving me back to Tyrone's, he told me he was sorry he "let things get so serious"

I told him he did not let things get serious

I told him he made things get serious

I am telling you what I told him

He told me other guys had wanted to date him since we had broken up, and he had to decline, because he was not ready, due to where he was at in his life

Driving through my neighborhood, he noted how "sketchy" it was

He parked and told me he would be at Trade on Saturday for beer bust

He hugged me and kissed where my neck met my jaw

It felt bad how good it felt

I texted him

"Thanks for trying to be friends—you're so Goddamn adorable"

I went to Trade

Ryan arrived with Ron

Somehow, the subject of judgment came up in conversation

Ryan was talking about judgment in a negative way, saying it was wrong to judge other people

I told him he was judging judgment, that everybody was judging everything all the time

"Well there's judgment and then there's *judgment*—there's measuring and discerning, and there's judging someone's character"

I found this ironic, because, on the subject of the verbal expression of love, Ryan had once told me he showed his love predominantly with his actions, not his words

And your actions constituted your character

And if you did shitty things that hurt people, they would judge your character

It seemed like it was not judgment of character that Ryan had issues with, but rather being held responsible for his actions as an adult, to which he took great offense when faced with their consequences—penal or not

I asked Ryan if I could tell him something

I told him I knew he was still attracted to me

He told me we could not keep doing this

"I don't mean to be harsh, Ben, but you got really clingy and that was a red flag"

He and Ron left

He texted me

"I need space, man—please give it to me [prayer hands emoji]"

"You can have all the space in the world you need, 'man'—it just sucks to be the emotional collateral damage of a man-child who doesn't know what he wants—you will continue to have half-feelings in half-relationships and superficial, drug-based friendships—you will wake one morning after weeks at your new generosity-as-career job, and you will realize that it has nothing at all to do with being a good person—there is no love here—you are spoiled garbage"

The next morning, I texted him

"Hey, that was really horrible and shitty—I'm so sorry—we clearly need to spend time apart—if I see you out, I'll be nice and friendly—good luck to you—sorry again"

A week later, he texted me

"Yes, it was terrible and shitty, and at this point, the apology doesn't mean much—I'm not interested in being nice or friendly—I'm done—if we see each other, a curt 'hello' or nod is more than enough—ignoring each other is fine as well—good luck to you, too—I'm blocking all electronic communication from this point forward if you have not already done so"

I got in trouble at Honey for doing a bump in the bathroom stall with Hips

The guy working security caught us

"One to a stall!"

He snitched on me to management to try to get me fired and take my shifts, but it backfired on him and he quit

I got called into the office after a staff meeting

"Is this bad?"

"It's not good"

The manager told me "everybody gets one" and that he would have immediately fired me if I had not helped get the bar ready for weeks before it opened

He told me he loved me, I told him I loved him, and we hugged

I moved in with Scorpio and Lad—all my things were still in boxes and I was not unpacking them now

I found Dean on Scruff

Dr. Dean Campbell

Just what the doctor ordered

He was visiting Denver

I went to his hotel room and fucked the shit out of him (in the good way)

His asshole was very tight, and when I came, it felt like it was squeezing the opening of my penis shut and the fluid was trapped inside

Painful!

We got dinner at Steuben's after

He told me about how he and his husband had a mostly transactional partnership, that he went on trips like these alone to have fun

I told him about the meeting with my father

He told me I should let go of the crimes of the past, if I could

Damn

Thanks, daddy

I told him I had a book come out earlier that year

"You wrote a book?"

"Yessir"

"That sounds haaarrrd"

I texted Norm a picture of Dean in a kimono he wore at some point during a business trip to Japan

"Damn—he looks like Ryan if he went on a quest to become a man"

Leslie and Connor flew into town for the two readings they had booked for me and others

I was happy George got to read

One of the readers on the first night's lineup was a former professor of mine from Naropa

Because of my pen name, he did not know I was reading with him

Surprise!

"So how's the writer life been for you, Ben?"

"Writer life . . . I don't know"

Leslie put herself on both readings' lineups

Before the second reading, she hit George's vape pen and got gourded

The venue was a combination bookstore/bar with kombucha on tap

SOMETHING GROSS

When it was her turn to read, she wore sunglasses and read the blurbs from her book

Like, as the reading, she read the blurbs from her book

George was talking during it

I told him to shut up

Shut up, George—I know this is the most embarrassing thing you have ever seen, but you have to be quiet while others read

After, I overheard Connor reassuring her

". . . Yeah, I think people liked it—it was very different—I don't think I've ever seen anyone do that at a reading before"

I went to a diner with Leslie and Connor

She told me she "loved diners"

At our table, I saw her trying to sneak a picture of me

I stared her down until she put her phone away

Pride 2019 and the Subsequent Spiral

I was walking through City Park, talking to Peaches on the phone

"You know, I think for the first time I'm really feeling Gay Pride—it's in the air—it's really joyful"

"Who are you and what have you done with Ben?"

I got a letter in the mail from my father

It was a card with an illustration of a whale on it

The inside of the card read "Have a whale of a birthday!"

There was a check for two hundred dollars

The price of an eight-ball

I went home with a thick bottom bear the first night of Pride
and fucked him

He blurted out "I love you" during it

He told me it was an accident, and he did not mean it

On the second day, in the car to a Pride BBQ with Jaime, he told
me what was going on in the Bless's Messes group text

Ryan received a package of my book in the mail—the book's cover
had a bouquet of yellow roses wrapped in barbed wire—I had
consulted him on the design

"This came in the mail—do I dare open it?—what if there's
ANTHRAX?"

"I'm honestly surprised he hasn't sent you letters"

"I guess when you block someone electronically, they go old
school"

Ryan had asked Jaime what he was doing that day, he told me,
and told him he was hanging out with me

"Gross—we can meet up later"

I asked Jaime if he thought Ryan meant that as in my surname, or as in "ew"

He told me he likely meant it as in "ew"

Jaime told me he hooked up with the same guy as Ryan, this little top Miguel

I tried to imagine Miguel topping Ryan, but I could only picture a kid jumping up and down on a beanbag

Jaime told me the other night at Trade, he pulled Ryan aside

"Hey girl—I have something to tell you"

"What's up?"

"So I kind of hooked up with someone . . ."

"—Ben!"

"Uh, no girl—Miguel"

"Oh"

"Yeah, you kind of oversold him"

Jaime told me Miguel took forever to come, that he kept

getting overheated from the medication he was on and had to take breaks

"Ryan was so ready to think we fucked—who does he think we are . . . him?"

We laughed

We had fun at the BBQ

There were slip-n-slides

I accidentally took a sip from a can of beer that was being used as an ashtray

Jaime left to meet up with Ryan and the Messes

I saw them at Paul's bear dance party that night

Ron gave me a "you fucked up" look as we passed in the crowd

I went to the Honcho party after

It was in the same warehouse as the rave

I entered the dark room, separating the plastic flaps with my hands and arms

There were a lot of guys having sex with each other

Not a condom in sight

I saw Bernard getting sandwiched by two daddy bears in leather harnesses

I saw a guy fisting two ass-up guys on a couch simultaneously

He was alternating, pumping his arms like pistons and torquing his torso, working the obliques

Hips had a "Skittles bag" of pressed ecstasy

I started chain-smoking cigarettes after having not smoked for years

A guy gave me a fist-bump because we were wearing the same jockstrap

"Jockstrap brothers!"

I went to the bathroom and noticed I had shit on my arm

I did not know how it got there

I went home with a guy who had already taken two loads from other guys that night

SOMETHING GROSS

On the third day, I went to a rooftop party with Jaime

We met an Australian guy and his faghag

She had a big bag of ketamine, and I did a few bumps

"You don't look good, boo"

I was pale and queasy, breaking out in cold sweats

I went home

On the fourth day, Father's Day, I worked beer bust

I saw Ryan as he was waiting in line to go to the upstairs patio

My twenty-ninth birthday was the Tuesday after Pride, and very few people showed because they were all still hungover

Jaime moved home to Seattle

I worked four happy hours per week

Pablo, Ryan's handsy friend, was a cocaine dealer

I bought from him frequently

He dressed like he lived in Miami

"The regular shit is eighty for a g, and the fire shit is a hundred fifty"

"Is it that good?"

"It's straight from the whore's stomach"

"Damn"

"Don't do too much—you'll start thinking people are out to get you"

We came up with a code—"tacos" meant regular and "spicy tacos" meant fire

He started showing at the end of my shifts, when I had a pocket full of cash

"Hey Ben, you hungry?"

I served Miguel at Honey

"Hey, do you know my friend Ryan?"

"Yeah, that's my ex"

"I thought so"

"I know you guys hang out—I don't have the best things to say about him"

"Yeah . . . I got really infatuated with him, and then he just cut me off"

I was in Pablo's car, lamenting the situation with Ryan

"I don't think he ever wants to talk to me again"

"I mean . . . do you blame him?"

"No"

"I keep thinking I want to move back to Wisconsin, to be around my mom, but then I think about what I'll be giving up here"

"If you feel like you get enough contact with her over FaceTime, then stay"

I told him about my coworker snitching on me

"That's shitty"

I saw Chad at Trade

He told me he took Ryan to the Colorado Symphony

He told me Ryan told him taking him to the Symphony did not make up for all the cocaine he had given him

He told me Ryan had a selective memory, that he had forgotten all the cocaine he had given him when he was in grad school a decade ago

He told me Ryan took what he wanted, regardless of the consequences of who it hurt

He told me he had caught Ryan lying to him multiple times

He told me Ryan would never be happy because he was not able to accept love

He told me Ryan would sometimes talk about me when they were hanging out

"I wonder what my ex-boyfriend is doing tonight"

SOMETHING GROSS

It was trivia night, and I had just clocked out

Ryan and Pablo were a trivia tandem called "Shits and Giggles"

I was on a trivia team called "You Smell Like My Dad"

I went up to Ryan, putting my hand on his back

"Hey . . . ex-boyfriend"

"Hey Ben"

"I'm really sorry"

"Hey, I'm not perfect either—I'm not really in the mood to chat—I'm gonna keep hanging out with Pablo"

"Okay"

"I heard you got busted"

He laughed

Pablo had told Ryan what I told him in confidence, I guessed

I bought them shots

I saw Ryan and Pablo at Trade

I turned around and sat down alone with a cigarette

Ryan approached me

"Hey, I don't want you to think I'm being rude—I just don't want to be social with you—you're smoking?"

"Yeah"

"Thanks for the shots"

They went across the street to Gladys and I followed them

I approached Ryan

"Hey—not that you owe me any consideration, but when I saw you at Honey and you—"

"Oh yeah, I made that crack about you getting busted—sorry"

"Yeah—that was a low point for me, and you brought it up right at the bar, in front of my coworkers"

"Well, it turned out fine—you bounced back"

"Yeah . . ."

"I'm sorry I was so mean to you"

"No one has ever talked to me like that before"

"I know!—I've never talked to anyone like that before"

"It's okay—when we don't get what we want, it makes us insecure—an apology just doesn't mean much now"

"Yeah . . ."

"It's okay—it's over—you work on you and I'll work on me"

"Okay . . ."

"How's your mom?"

I laughed, looking at the floor

"Steadily declining"

"I'm sorry, that sucks"

"How's the new job"

"It's alright—this 'rockstar lifestyle' is making it hard"

Outside, I saw Ryan drunkenly leave the bar

"Bye guys—make bad decisions—it's fun"

A few nights later, I could not sleep

I emailed Ryan's work address

> *I'm writing this but I don't know if I'm going to send it to you. Or how to send it to you. I really don't want to send this to your work email. My purpose of writing this is not out of the angry and hurt cruelty I threw against you more than twice. I'm doing this to try to bring understanding if nothing else. When I texted you that last time that you were "spoiled garbage," I wasn't hiding behind words. This is something you said I do, hide behind words. As vile as they were, they weren't there as a way of concealing, but as a portal into my private thoughts. I wrote that to you because that's how you made me feel. You made me feel, seemed to treat me like, garbage. Disposable. I felt disposed of by you. It felt like you used me up, took what you needed, then left. The last time we spoke at Gladys, you said, in reference to how I reacted and treated you, something like, "When we don't get what we want, we can get insecure." I have to counter this take on what happened, which makes it sound like I'm a petulant child who threw a tantrum. It's just not that simple, and this feels a gross reduction. If it was as simple as me not getting what I wanted, I wouldn't have reacted the way I did. It wasn't a feeling of insecurity. It was a feeling of being wronged, of being used, my trust betrayed, a disregard*

for my feelings. What I said wasn't a thorn sprung from a spurned ego.

I haven't forgiven myself, and won't for a long time, for how I wrote to you. The level of regret and shame I feel at times overtakes me. I made it so you'd never trust me again, to not hurt you in that way, and it breaks me up horribly to face that, which I have to do every day. I fell in love with you in such a hard way. I became vulnerable to you so fast. When I reached out to you after learning of my mom's diagnosis, not really knowing anybody else who had been through a thing like that, and you made yourself open to it, to talking about it, and your own experience with it, that bound us in parallel griefs, it seemed like. Later at Gladys, you asked me, "How's your mom?" When I bent over and laughed, it was because I didn't know what else to do. You've cut me out of your life completely. You said you were done with me. You don't want to be social. You said you weren't interested in being nice and friendly. But you brought up such a wound, and a wound that we share, in a way. You don't want to have anything to do with me, have erected the most thorough of boundaries, yet when I came to you at my bar, to be vulnerable in front of you and apologize, you asked me, "Oh, you know Levi and Daimeon?" After all that happened between us, I felt confused by this question. Why is someone who wants nothing to do with me so curious about who I know, who I'm spending my time with? Is this fishing for a gossip item? Why does the man who said he loved me, who sobbed in my arms as I held him naked, want to know how my mom,

*who is dying of basically the same thing that his mom died
of, is? If he truly wants to have nothing to do with me,
couldn't he assume that my dying mom is . . . dying? Is he
. . . just being polite?*

*It's like you want to care, but don't. Or can't right now. Or
are afraid to. If you want to care, then you should do that.
But don't eliminate someone from your life and then ask
him how his dying mom is. Or who he is friends with. Or
make fun of him for fucking up at work, taking pleasure in
something bad that happened, holding it over him. I know
I fucked up bad with how mean I was to you, but as mean
as it was, as self-righteous as it was, it came from a place of
being hurt, misled, and deceived. I'm sorry, but I just refuse
to believe that you merely thought you were in love with me,
and then wasn't. Those words didn't issue from a guess. It
was something you felt. Something you knew. Even if you
weren't ready to take on the responsibility—the promise, in
a way—those words implied, you meant what you said. I
refuse to believe you're that shallow.*

*I think what made me snap the last time was the thing
you said about how I was clingy and that raised a red flag.
The nerve, I thought. You'd think with the many red flags
you raised for me at the time: mid-forties and never had a
boyfriend/been in a long term relationship before, a regular
cocaine user and binge drinker, disrespectful to his bodily
health and the bodily health of others (I'm speaking of the
post-Valentine's Day gonorrhea debacle), flakes on like half*

the plans he makes if the plans don't already have tentative escape hatches built into them, and so on, and how I accepted and saw past those things to love you, the person . . . you'd think that you could extend that to me, despite my red flags.

No one has ever talked to you like I did, and I haven't ever talked to anyone like I did to you. I hadn't ever felt so discarded by another person—and to his relief, no less. It's my fault. I should have been way more careful in trying to reconcile things with you and be friends the last failed attempt. I was pushing down and holding back so much anger and hurt towards you for how I saw the way you treated me. How you treated me with your actions and regard. Not text messages. I didn't know how to tell you how you made me feel. I think I was trying to be calm. It's not a calm subject, though.

I'm going to stop going to trivia, and I'm going to try to stop going to Trade. I'm going to try to leave the bar right when I clock out. It hurts too bad and gives me too much anxiety to be in the same room as you, avoiding you. I'm punishing myself enough. I'm never going to talk to you that way again. It's always a risk, there's always trust on the line when you decide to care about someone other than yourself. But if you do it halfway, or are speaking your care through a hermetic boundary, you might as well not care at all. The effect is the same as not caring at all. It means about as much to me as my apology meant to you.

I was outside Gladys with this married bear I was seeing

Ryan, Pablo, and Chad showed

Chad approached me

"You've been a bad boy, Ben—Ryan's not happy—he was even talking about setting up an email you could talk to him through, too—someone from IT at his work could find that combing through while looking for something else—Ryan could get drug tested and fired"

"Yeah . . ."

Ryan approached me

"Hey, I wanna talk to you—I've been looking for you"

We walked down the sidewalk

"Sending that email was really not cool, Ben"

"—Yeah, that was bad"

"—Someone could find that and I could lose my job—who is that, the guy you're dating now or something?"

"He's my friend"

"Whatever—and you made me seem like such a bad person—I deleted the email and blocked your address—you need to leave me alone—it's going to be a zillion years before we can be friends—six months, a year—leave me alone—okay?"

"Sorry—okay"

I went across the street to Trade, and Pablo approached me

He was super high on cocaine, talking at me with wide eyes

He told me I was self-righteous and a hypocrite, that I binge drank and spent money I did not have on cocaine

He told me the email was vindictive

I told him it did not occur to me that the email could potentially get him fired

He told me he did not believe me

He told me next time I felt like writing something like that to not send it, to burn it, that I was a writer, to make it into art (thanks for the advice, Pablo—how am I doing so far?)

He told me he was telling me this as a friend

He told me he was "looking out for Pablo"

He gave me a bump in the bathroom

I was on Doc's porch, smoking and drinking

We had become fast friends after he bought my book from me and read it

He had sent me a long text about it, telling me where he thought I was "in my journey" and that it would be interesting to see where I would go

I was telling him about the Ryan stuff

"Oh yeah girl—I know who he is—he kind of looks like a lion"

"Well, he is a Leo"

"He hit me up on Scruff after he moved back here—sent me nudes and messaged me all manner of nasty shit—I know at least five people in the community he catfished with older pictures of himself from before he got fat—one guy told me he let him suck his dick because he felt sorry for him"

He gave me some of what he called "old gay black man wisdom"

He called Ryan a "domestic/emotional terrorist"

"Girl, you are in a love *mess*, a perception *mess*"

SOMETHING GROSS

I had done it

I was one of Bless's Messes

Like Ryan, I had become what hurt me

"Why are you friends with me?"

"I'd be stupid not to—what I've been trying to tell these boys is that you're brand new—we've never had someone like you in the group—an artist—also, you're just a good person—you're not fake"

I had my foot resting on the porch's concrete ledge, knee bent—I rapidly licked my lips

Doc gasped

"Oh my God—what the fuck was that?"

We were both laughing

"That's so gross—you just turned into a lizard—I saw it flash across your face . . . the lizard—don't EVER do that again"

It became a running gag between us—I would occasionally lick my lips like a fiendish serpent during conversational lulls

I went to Wisconsin in September—she was worse

I drove to Michigan to spend a night at Norm's

I had not seen him since the road trip with Joey

He walked out to his apartment complex's parking lot to greet me and I was smoking a cigarette

I told him I had talked to Doc for over an hour on the phone while driving out there

I told him Doc told me Ryan had thrown himself at Doc at Honey, shoving his hands down his shirt and pants, telling him "you know you're the most handsome guy in this bar"

I told him Ryan knew I was out of town, and that he knew I was visiting my mother, and that he knew Doc and I were close

I told him Doc told Ryan "I'm not gonna put you on blast in front of the group, but I know where this is coming from—I know what this is about, and I'm not playing this game"

I told him Doc told me Ryan was taken aback, then tried to laugh it off

I told him I was glad I had at least one loyal friend in Denver

SOMETHING GROSS

It was great to see Norm

He seemed content living in the country, or at least more open than I had ever known him to be

He made me a chicken sandwich and got me stoned

We sat on his balcony, looking out over a large field

I told him more about the Ryan stuff

"... He played me, and I played myself"

"It happens to so many"

I stood to lean on the railing, and he stopped me

"—That's not secure, you'll fall"

He had my back

I was invited to New Orleans for a reading

A paid reading

I got to spend four nights with Peaches at his big, fancy house in the Garden District

He had been dating this guy

This trial lawyer who owned restaurants, with an adopted son

He was like a gay John Grisham protagonist

He was a thousand times better on paper than me

But Peaches was still in love with me

Despite having the option of everything he wanted

I wondered why that was

It was Halloween weekend

I was on the upstairs patio at Honey with Doc and his group

Hips was there, too

Chad showed and approached me

"The bitches are on their way"

It seemed like Chad would show to a bar before Ryan, to do reconnaissance

To scout and survey

SOMETHING GROSS

To see if I was there

To report back

To do Ryan's bidding, like a witch's flying monkey

Jim was there, too, so I talked to him in the corner

Ryan and the Messes arrived

I tried to ignore them

I heard Doc raise his voice

"Bobby—are you seeing this shit?—look at this trash"

I turned and looked across the patio at Doc

He was pointing at Hips, who was giving Pablo a back rub

"Straight fucking TRASH bro"

"Doc, calm down"

"Oh, I'm fine—I'm at about a 'two' right now"

He gestured toward the side of the patio Ryan was on

"Look Bobby—everyone on this side of the room is on coke—look at Hips's nose running—"

Hips quickly wiped his nose on the inside of his shirt collar

"Doc, please—I can see it, but please . . ."

He gestured toward the side of the patio I was on

"—And everyone on THIS side is emotionally damaged"

Pablo approached Doc, reaching his hand out to touch Doc's arm

"Hey, we're all friends here"

"Do NOT touch me—I'm not your fucking friend—you don't make enough money to talk to me, cokehead . . ."

Bobby looked horrified

"I feel like I'm losing my GODdamn mind—someone has to say this shit—"

He pointed directly at me

"—Cuz I know THIS motherfucker ain't gon' say SHIT—and you know what?—he don't have to"

He pointed directly at Ryan

"You are LUCKY that a person like that—"

He pointed back to me

"—Was with a person like YOU"

He pointed back to Ryan

"That doesn't happen in reality—THIS . . . IS . . . NOT . . . REALITY!"

He lit a menthol extra long

A couple black guys approached Doc, attempting to de-escalate

"Nigga don't talk to me just cuz you're black and I'm black—Jesus fucking Christ—tryna calm me down for these white people—coon ass nigga"

Ryan and the Messes left

It was Sunday beer bust, about an hour before the end of my shift

Zac approached my service area

"Hey man—you gonna be around after your shift?"

"Yeah, I'll probably hang out for a bit"

"Alright—there's something I wanna talk to you about"

"Oh yeah, what's up?"

"I'll talk to you when you get off"

"It's not busy—I can talk . . . what's going on man?"

"Brentford killed himself"

Upstairs at Honey, Pablo approached me and I reluctantly engaged him in conversation

He asked me how I was doing

I told him I wasn't doing too well, that my friend hanged himself on Halloween and his husband discovered him in the bathroom

"I'm sorry for your pain"

I went on about it

"Yeah . . . the world is fucked up and crazy—sorry, I've been around a lot of death, so I'm not the best person to talk to about it"

I was smoking a cigarette outside Honey after my shift

Jaime texted me

"Gurl, I have some T for you"

"Oh yeah?—is it gonna hurt my feelings?"

"Ryan and Andy hooked up"

My ex had sucked one of his best friend's ex's dicks after he moved to Seattle

His friend's ex, who beat up his friend while they were together

His friend, whom he drove to court

So much for "girl code"

What a timeline in which we had found ourselves

What a gay world

What a mess

I felt sorry for Jaime

I felt sorry for Ryan

I felt sorry for Andy

I felt sorry for myself

I told Doc about it at Z bar

I was on my knees, hysterical

He was genuinely shocked

"Oh my God . . . that truly is T"

"Yeah dude"

"I don't even know what to say to that . . . that's two people manifesting so much negativity"

"So much spite . . . he probably did it because he thought Jaime and I fucked, or maybe he was just upset we became friends"

"Gurrrl . . ."

I fucked a daddy bear in Lakewood who was a percussionist—I fucked a daddy bear Gulf War veteran in Thornton who appeared to be a militant Zionist based on his bedside literature—I fucked a black bear on East Colfax—I fucked a cub while his husband was asleep upstairs and I was so high on coke I nutted inside him four times taking cigarette breaks in between—I fucked a daddy who looked like an athletic Santa Claus at the DSC in a private room—I fucked a thick ginger cub in Highland who was in an open relationship—I ran into Zangief at Trade and he told me he had always had a crush on me and I told him I had always had a crush on him, so I throatfucked him and spent the night while Bernard was out of town for a gay rugby tournament and probably fucking/getting fucked by a bunch of guys himself—Zangief told me I was depressed and reminded him of his ex who killed himself—I asked Zangief "what about Ryan" and he said "fuck Ryan—I'd pick you as a friend over him any day"—I fucked a chub daddy bear who told me he had smoked meth before I arrived—I fucked a thin ginger who lived near Honey—I fucked a daddy in Capitol Hill who said he was friends with Grace Jones's sister, then helped him put a piece of furniture in the back of his truck in the morning—I fucked a thick otter in Capitol Hill—I saw Ryan push his head into a guy's chest at Trade—I got chlamydia and fucked a guy the day after getting treated—I ran into Elf Boots, his wife, and teenage son in Capitol Hill while doing a "walk of shame"—I fucked a daddy bear who had MS and a limited range of motion—I got recognized at urgent care by an RN like "back again?"—I got chlamydia again—I dated a guy, made him get really into me, then ghosted him—I fucked a daddy bear who played the French horn and told him I wanted to date him, then changed my mind—I fucked a daddy bear

"Could I call you 'daddy' and you call me 'son' and tell me you love me, even though you don't mean it?"

"Sure—I can do that for you, son"

I was having a beer after working Sunday beer bust at Honey and Mervin approached me

Mervin had effectively replaced Jaime in the Messes

I told him I heard about Ryan and Andy hooking up

He told me it really upset him, and that he "caught" them doing it

He told me he took a picture of them, so nobody could tell him it did not happen

"At least Ryan texted Jaime about it, told him first so he didn't have to find out—Jaime told me Ryan told him 'it only lasted for like five minutes and nobody came' . . . as if that matters . . . as if that's the point"

He had been courting Andy since Jaime left, even took him on vacation

But Andy was not interested

Mervin ended up throwing a bottle of liquor at Andy after he found him getting his dick sucked by Ryan

He told me he did not like the way the Messes had labeled me, my character

He was clearly coming onto me, getting handsy

I left

Dana was cutting my hair, giving me a fade

I told her about Ryan, my father, my mother, and everything else

"Oh my God—Ben—babe—can you please step out of the line of fire?"

I would step out of the line of fire, Dana, if it was not so wide

It was more like a lane than a line

At Scorpio's, in the mirror, I noticed my head was covered in lesions

Peaches had a longer layover at DIA

I took the train out to visit with him

He noticed I was limping

I told him I had gotten a Penicillin shot for syphilis

He scolded me, told me he was worried

He cleaned the psoriasis plaques from my ears with cotton swabs

We made out

I told him I loved him and wanted to be with him

He told me he did, too, but was having a really hard time trusting me after everything I had put him through

Dinah had an even longer layover on her way to Hawaii, for Christmas

We got brunch

She told me about the fallout of Orson's death, how traumatic it was for her to have her house transformed into a hospice

She told me about how Olivia's second, Otto, had been born

She told me Olive told her about her father

"My dad . . . he's dead—but it's okay because he's in the spirit world now"

I am telling you what she told me

I called Joey and told him what Olive had told Dinah about Orson

We laughed

Scorpio told me I had to move out as soon as possible

She told me I had really hurt her

She told me I had not kept my word to her as a roommate and a friend

She told me I had not noticed how hurt she was, because of how "wrapped up in my own shit" I was

I told her she was right

I told her I was sorry

I told her I would move out as soon as possible

I called Dinah and told her I wanted to move back to Wisconsin

I told her I did not want my mother or grandmother to "see me like this"

I asked her if I could stay with her for a while

"No more than a couple months"

She told me I could

I thanked her

I gave the owners and management of Honey my notice

They told me they understood

They told me they loved me

They told me the door would always be open for me should I ever return

They wished me the best

I called Joey and told him I was moving back to Wisconsin

He told me he was glad and relieved

I had a threesome

SOMETHING GROSS

I figured if it was ever going to happen, now was the time

It was an interracial married couple—a black guy and a white guy, both named Jack

Black Jack had already sucked my dick in the bathroom at Trade before

I fucked white Jack while black Jack stared deeply into his husband's eyes

"You like that, baby?—you like getting fucked by that big dick?—I'm so proud of you"

He tapped me

"Mind if I have a turn?"

"Sure"

Yes, black Jack, you may have a turn having sex with your husband

Pablo was missing

I saw Ryan and the Messes upstairs at Honey

I did not want to be around them

As I exited the patio, I saw Ryan pantomiming doing a line of cocaine and sucking a dick

They got quiet

I squeezed past them

A few paces after I passed them, I heard them cackling—Ryan the loudest of all

Downstairs, I was talking to Cockie, a coworker of mine—this journeyman bartender who had been in scene after scene

I told him what was going on

"That's your ex?—oh, I don't like her"

He told me he helped start the bear dance parties with Paul years ago, and that for one of the recent Denver parties, his friend who was hired to dance, a "go-go bear," was planning on staying with Ryan

He told me his friend told Ryan, closer to the time of his flight to Denver, that he would just be staying at Ryan's apartment, and no sex would be had between the two of them

He told me Ryan ghosted the go-go bear and left him stranded at the airport, and he called Cockie, and he had to pick him up himself

Walking to the bus stop outside the bar, somebody yelled at me from a car

"BIG BRUISER DOPE BOY!"

I flinched, then looked to see who it was

It was the guy who had set up and hosted the reading at Mutiny

I ran over to the car, smiling

"Hey man, thanks for saying hi"

I gave him a fist bump

I was upstairs at Honey

I wanted to give a bag of cocaine back to my friend Thomas, but he was talking to Ryan

I looked at Thomas, pointed down, and mouthed "I'll meet you downstairs"

Thomas told me Ryan turned to him after I went downstairs

"Oh my God, that's my ex"

Thomas did not know we were exes

Ryan seemed to love claiming me as his ex-boyfriend to others

See that guy?—that hot guy over there—that's my ex—we don't talk—he's crazy—he's volatile—he's explosive

We were never boyfriends

We were never even friends

What were we?

We were a mess

Thomas told me he told Ryan I was going to Wisconsin to take care of some family stuff

"What?—do you know if he's coming back?"

He did not know I was moving

I had thought he might have heard

I asked Thomas if he could relay a message to Ryan for me

"Could you just tell him I'm sorry, I care about him a lot, and

I wish him the best?"

"Of course I will, boo"

The End of The Book

Is January 2020

I am driving back to Wisconsin in a rented minivan with all my
things in it

The boxes I never unpacked

It is late, and I have about an hour left before I get to Dinah's

I am on the phone with Peaches

I am crying

I am screaming at him

My throat hurts from it

I am telling him I am sorry

He is telling me how much I hurt him, how I deceived him over and over while trying to be with Ryan

He is telling me how angry he is at Ryan, for taking me away from him

"HE DIDN'T TAKE ME AWAY FROM YOU!—I FELL IN LOVE WITH HIM!—I CHOSE HIM OVER YOU!—IT'S MY FAULT!—I'M SORRY!—I DIDN'T WANT TO GET BACK TOGETHER WITH YOU BECAUSE YOU HURT ME SO BAD WHEN YOU BROKE UP WITH ME!—HOW AM I SUPPOSED TO TRUST YOU IF YOU ENDED OUR RELATIONSHIP BECAUSE YOU WEREN'T GETTING EVERYTHING YOU WANTED?!"

"'EVERYTHING I WANTED'?!—IT WAS LIKE PULLING TEETH TO GET YOU TO DO ANYTHING!—GOING TO THE MOVIES, GOING TO PARTIES, GETTING ON AIRPLANES!—YOU NEVER TRIED BOTTOMING ONCE!—I CHANGED MY WHOLE FUCKING LIFE FOR YOU!—I MOVED TO BOULDER TO BE WITH YOU WHILE YOU WENT TO SCHOOL!"

"I WENT TO SCHOOL BECAUSE YOU TOLD ME YOU 'WOULDN'T HITCH YOUR WAGON TO SOMEONE WITHOUT A DEGREE'!—I'M NOT SOME FUCKING LOSER POET, YOU KNOW!—I'M A GOOD PERSON AND I HAVE A LOT TO OFFER!—I KNOW THERE ARE

CERTAIN THINGS I HAVE TROUBLE WITH, AND SOME THINGS I CAN'T DO AT ALL, BUT I NEVER TRIED TO MAKE YOU DO OR BE *ANYTHING* YOU DIDN'T WANT TO DO OR BE!—I WAS CONSTANTLY AFRAID YOU WERE GOING TO LEAVE ME BECAUSE I WASN'T GOOD ENOUGH FOR YOU!—YOU WERE ALWAYS CONTROLLING ME!"

"YOU CONTROLLED EVERYTHING WE DID!—YOU SAID 'NO' TO EVERYTHING!"

"SO FUCKING WHAT?!—SO WHAT IF I HATE PARTIES!—I LOVED YOU AND ACCEPTED YOU FOR WHO YOU WERE!—YOU WERE ALWAYS TRYING TO FASHION ME INTO SOMEONE I WASN'T TO SATISFY YOURSELF!—CAN'T YOU SEE HOW FUCKING SUPERFICIAL THAT IS?!"

"FINE, BEN!—YOU'RE A BETTER PERSON THAN ME, OKAY!—IS THAT WHAT YOU WANT ME TO SAY?!"

"NO!—I JUST WANT YOU TO LET THAT SHIT GO BECAUSE IT'S HURTING YOU!!!"

We calm down

I have been parked in Dinah's driveway for a half-hour

I am exhausted

SOMETHING GROSS

I have deteriorated

I tell Peaches I love him forever

He tells me the same

I tell him I will call him tomorrow

We end the call

I cry

The movement of the long trip is over, but I am still moving fast

I do my best to collect myself, and get out of the minivan

I open the always-unlocked door of Dinah's house and feebly announce my presence

Her small dogs run up and greet me with piercing, high-pitched barks

She enters from the other room

"Shut up you ugly little rats! Hey lil fella, you made it . . ."

I start sobbing

"Oh, oh, oh—come here"

She hugs me and I hold onto her

"I'm sorry . . . it's really great to see you . . . I just went through some bad things and I'm in a lot of pain right now . . . I'm sorry . . . thank you for letting me stay here . . . I'm sorry . . . I'm sorry"

I am sorry I lost my way

Epilogue

Sandhill Cranes

For years, when visiting the Southern Wisconsin River Valley, I would encounter a pair of sandhill cranes near my grandparents' house

Slender, elegant, reddish-brown, clicking in unison

Peaches once told me that a pair will stay together year after year

Which meant that, each time, it was probably the same pair I had seen

The other day, I was driving along the county trunk highways in what used to be my grandfather's car

Not driving anywhere in particular, just clearing my head

I turned onto T and was about to pass the house my grandparents did not live in anymore, my grandfather dead for nine years and my grandmother living alone in town

At the edge of the marsh by the side of the road were sandhill cranes

I braked to a creep, making sure in the rearview nobody was coming

There were three of them, one smaller than the other two

For a minute or so, they moved slowly and watched me as I moved slowly and watched them—I had never before seen three together

I saw a car approaching in the mirror and left

ACKNOWLEDGMENTS

Grateful acknowledgment is made to the editors of the publications in which the writing in this book originally appeared (some in different form and under different titles):

Muumuu House: "The Road Trip with Joey"
Young Magazine: "The First Time Ryan Told Me He Loved Me"

With gratitude to Joey Russo and Sam Pink.

ABOUT THE AUTHOR

Big Bruiser Dope Boy is the author of *Foghorn Leghorn, Your First Real Boyfriend & Other Poems*, and *After Denver*.

Printed in Great Britain
by Amazon

65349342R00149